Japan Surges Ahead

Japan Surges Ahead

The Story of an Economic Miracle

P. B. Stone

Frederick A. Praeger, *Publishers*

New York · Washington

BOOKS THAT MATTER

Published in the United States of America in 1969
by Frederick A. Praeger, Inc., Publishers
111 Fourth Avenue, New York, N.Y. 10003

Library of Congress Catalog Card Number: 71-75417

Printed in Great Britain

TO JENN
and her cottages

Contents

Acknowledgments

My thanks are due first to the publishers of the now defunct *Statist* at whose expense I was able to visit Japan. A good deal of this book is based on research I carried out as Science Correspondent of that magazine. My thanks are also due to Norman Macrae, deputy editor of the *Economist* on whose own material I have drawn very heavily for six chapters of this book. But for his detailed coverage of subjects like the bureaucracy, banking, trading houses and labour policies in the *Economist* it would have been impossible even to attempt a balanced coverage of Japan's advance.

In Japan my thanks are due above all to Mr Tammy Yiu of Sun Gain Shia who was my helper, travel agent and skilful 'fixer'. I must also acknowledge the help of Messrs Eijiro Fujise and Kaizo Hashimoto of Jetro, and Keiichi Tachibana at Foreign Affairs; Tokinsuke Murao, Akira Toyoji and Michio Sigemi at Toyo Kogyo; Hanzo Omi of Fujitsu; Ken Coach of Olympus Optical; and Hisashi Harada of JRDC; Seiji Hirobe and Takayoshi Nitta of Mitsubishi. Special thanks also to Duncan Fraser of Rolls Royce and Isaac Taira of *Wing*. I must also thank Dr Noboru Takagi, Professor Itogawa and Professor Kimura for giving me so much of their time. I ought to mention many other people in Japan who gave me boundless hospitality and a great deal of time but to do so would be perhaps embarrassing to them because it would reveal the origin of information not widely available.

My thanks are also due to E. A. Mason of ICI whose knowledge of Japan's chemical industry was most helpful and to M. Voice of BISRA.

In London, grateful thanks are due to M. Okamoto and John Larrett at Jetro, without whose help I would have been able to do very little. Last of all may I thank the anonymous young student in Kyoto who rescued me from a four-mile foot slog to the railway station on a crowded Sunday afternoon without a taxi in sight. He put me on the right tram and I have never felt quite so grateful.

Introduction

What people think of Japan depends greatly on their age. The oldest of all still have the cherry blossom and geisha image but those whose most impressionable years coincided with the thirties will remember the flood of cheap copies of western goods. The Pacific War brings memories of the infamy of Pearl Harbour, the ferocity of the Japanese Army and the horror of the prisoner of war camps. For today's youth, Japan's economic performance is becoming the dominant image. Even the economists who strive for exactitude have to use the language of theology to describe it and they, like any other observer, call it a miracle – they can describe it, but they cannot say how or why it happened.

Japan has emerged so brilliantly and swiftly that if only other nations like India, Brazil or China could do the same, the gulf between rich and poor, which threatens the stability of the world, could well be closed in the foreseeable future. As an economic freak Japan is of interest not only to the poor but to the rich as well. Indeed, to call nations like Britain or France rich is to use the word in a purely relative way for there are millions of people in Western Europe whose standard of living is a long way short of what their own middle classes would call comfortable. A British working man of twenty-five years of age cannot expect to double his real earnings until he is fifty. A Japanese working man can expect it in seven or eight years – that is what an economic miracle feels like to an ordinary person.

This is the reason why, just as wars are too important to be left to the soldiers, so economic miracles are too important to be left to the study of economists. In any case what has happened in Japan has been influenced by many factors other than superb economic management on the part of the Government. Japan's resurgence certainly has been helped by such things as sensitive manipulation of the bank rate, tariff walls and Government loans and by sophisticated planning and statistical services; but the character of her working people and the appropriateness of their traditions has been enormously significant too. Some observers have discerned a quite different source of vitality in Japan's industrial tycoons, the 'miracle men', as Ralph Hewins calls them in a recent book, like Matsushita, Honda and Idemitsu. Other more cynical students of human nature have noted that since Japan has been under the shadow of the United States and has been in no position to think of imperial expansion all her energies have gone into getting rich, a process made easier by not having to spend anything on defence.

Whatever the basic reasons, Japan is a fascinating economic laboratory. Since it is not usually possible to conduct experiments in the social sciences, the best one can do is to find unusual situations and see what happens to the observed regularities or the laws of economics. There are many occasions when economists and politicians prescribe apparently reasonable measures to correct some defect in a country's economic performance. Britain, being at the bottom of the international league tables of growth, is particularly exposed to advice from such experts. At present, for example, many of Britain's problems are ascribed to high levels of direct taxation, whereas some years ago insufficient expenditure on research and development was a favourite diagnosis. In both areas a very good case could be made out – until Japan was mentioned. What appeared to be a reasonable 'law' was then seen to have a bizarre exception, and the suggested measures were subsequently advocated with less force and more caution.

What is the best way to put over a balanced picture of Japan's industrial growth? It is a story with many loose ends, many unanswered questions and many obscure corners. Neither the view from the Government planner's office, from the tycoon's suite, the working man's shop floor, nor the European agent's Tokyo office can give anything but a partial impression. Taking these in some sort of logical order however does seem to promise the possibility of fair coverage, of putting flesh on the bare bones of statistics and of giving some feel for the country in its period of rapid change. With these aims in mind I have begun with a chapter to set the scene, an attempt to communicate instant Japan, an outline of the facts that any visitor to the country or any reader of this book needs to know. Then follow a few chapters which dip into Japan's technology; these give some feeling of the well-known industrial successes like shipbuilding, but I have also tried to show that Japan can make a mess of things in spite of good intentions – her attempt to get a satellite into orbit is one such misfortune. Having provided some idea of the physical reality of spreading industrial enterprise I have turned to the economic institutions which help to create the business climate. The book then returns to some of the notable sectors of the Japanese economy: steel, cameras, and the world-famous railways. What of the future, will Japan be able to go on with her surging growth? All the familiar problems of classical economics are there: the shortage of labour, the balance of payments, the exhaustion of natural resources (Japan never had any to speak of anyway) and the technology gap.

Lastly some attempt is made to plumb the depths of the Japanese character, or at least those facets of it that matter when it comes to the creation of physical wealth. The book ends with a chapter looking to the future in which every possible attempt is made to avoid drawing morals – except for just one.

There are lessons to be learnt from Japan but they are not very easy to express with confidence. Japan is rather like a philosopher; to get the full value, actual contact is necessary and even then there is much that is elusive. When I was at Oxford, I can remember arguing with students of philosophy about Bergson. I held up my end for a whole hour in some argument about this man's views (I was a scientist) until my opponent said in exasperation, 'If you really felt the spirit of the man, you could never say that, he is so humane.' I replied that I had only read critiques of Bergson and a potted account of the great man's thought in Russell's *History of Western Philosophy*. This produced profound shock in my opponent, a reaction which rapidly changed to contempt as the full extent of my deception became plain. I was made to feel that the true savour of a philosopher could only be sensed by reading him, if possible in his original language, otherwise some sort of *je ne sais quoi* would forever elude me. I am still unwilling to believe this of a philosopher's work but I find myself bound to assert that something of the same thing does apply to Japan.

One thing that unsettles anyone writing about Japan is the knowledge that the nation has executed the most violent changes of course with little warning and these have frequently taken other nations by surprise. The Japanese face is capable of concealing almost anything. It provides a human parallel to Japan's geological situation: it is well known that the islands' apparently solid structure is subject to violent earthquakes.

There is no doubt however about the physical reality of Japan's growing industrial wealth. Whatever is simmering in the political consciousness of Japan, the motor factories, the power-stations, the ports, the roads, the machine tools and the consumer durables are there for all to see. The desire for material comfort and stability is now strong in Japan and it must soon act as a sort of sea-anchor controlling the response of Japan to the storms which its own national character so frequently appears to cause.

So let us turn from the more elemental factors in man's nature and begin to look at something that, given enough understanding, ought to be capable of scientific control. The problem is how to organise large numbers of people to make the best of the benefits that modern science and technology seem to promise. Some nations do this badly, some do it well; so far the Japanese seem to have done it supremely well.

ONE

Instant Japan

In Japanese towns and cities they do not name the streets or number the houses consecutively. If you wish to find a particular address you go to the district and explore it until you find the place you want. The last moves are usually accomplished by asking the local inhabitants, since neither the postmen nor the taxi-drivers can be relied upon.

The visiting westerner, who has heard stories of Japanese efficiency and enterprise, finds this hard to believe and in the hotel bars it is common to hear recent arrivals asking their hosts if the Government is going to do anything about it. The answer is no, and when the American Occupation ceased, the Japanese actually took down the street signs the Americans had put up. There are various ways of describing this sort of behaviour. The Americans call it ornery and the British enigmatic, but in fact it reflects something in the Japanese character which is so consistent, widespread and inexplicable that you might as well give up looking for the right word and just call it Japanese.

The difficulty of 'understanding' the Japanese starts right at the roots with the Japanese language itself. Those mathematicians and astronomers who think they will be able to communicate with Martians and alien peoples from distant galaxies by means of a language based on prime numbers could well start with a terrestrial exercise in Japan. The stock trade joke amongst translators is that most Japanese sentences could have *not* inserted into them without really altering their meaning. In English translation, therefore, Japanese publications, articles and letters have a rare mistiness about them. As in Chinese paintings it is very difficult to tell how things are connected to each other and you never know what lies beyond the wisps and vapours of politeness and circumlocution.

Japanese is an ambiguous language in both the spoken and written forms and any kind of subtle communication is very difficult. However some things in life are simple, like asking the train times or ordering a meal; so an intending visitor who has enough mental energy to spare may be advised to learn a little. Books called *Instant Japanese* or *Japanese in Ten Hours* are, of course, even more mistitled than they would be if they were trying to teach Italian or German.

Japanese is quite unrelated to Chinese and is easier to pronounce than French. In understanding spoken Japanese the main problem is to develop a very short-term memory store. For instance, a word which is the subject of a sentence is identified by a suffix like 'wa' or 'ga'. On hearing the suffix one needs to remember the word *preceding* it because that is the important word. Similarly the verb is frequently constructed with something like 'to make' but this too is a suffix so again one needs to remember the previous word. Unfortunately there are usually many redundant polite qualifications in the sentence and the important word is often swamped; so getting this short-term memory is a difficult trick. But once acquired one has a solitary finger-hold on everyday Japanese.

A helpful feature is that many English words have been imported unchanged like, *bed, boat-race, Diesel, rocket, taxi* or *toilet paper;* others, however, are pronounced oddly, *waishatsu* is a much altered *white shirt*.

Simple sentences can be achieved. 'Watakshi-wa hako-wo ake-masu' means 'I (subject-wa) a box (object-wo) open make' or 'I open a box'. One soon runs out of initial enthusiasm however, not just because of illogicalities like the word order or the absence of the future tense, but because there is no feedback or reinforcement from being able to recognise written Japanese. Both notations, Chinese ideograms and Kana, are formidable barriers to reading the language and they are formidable hindrances to the Japanese themselves. Although spoken Japanese has nothing in common with Chinese, Japan did borrow Chinese characters for writing the language down. Over two thousand of these characters or ideograms are in common use and each one is composed of up to twenty-five different strokes of the pen or brush. A Japanese typewriter has over two thousand characters on the keyboard with many more in reserve. The machines are comparatively rare and are so complicated that one of the greatest commercial systems in the world just has to run on handwritten letters. Neon signs and advertisements come in Chinese ideograms, kata kana or hira gana (more or less phonetic notations with over forty letters each) or a mixture of all three, so that walking around a Japanese city does not give one any opportunity to reinforce one's vocabulary by reading the signs.

However, if it were not for the notices and adverts, a walk around a Japanese city would be little different from a walk in any other man-made canyon of concrete, steel, glass and noisy traffic. As in Britain and India, the traffic is on the left, and is more dangerous than anywhere else in the world. Inside a city the symbols of tourist Japan need looking for because the cherry trees, the stone lanterns and the Shinto shrines are no more in evidence in modern Japan than are thatched cottages and Beefeaters in Britain.

Among other things which will strike the Western visitor will be the proliferation of portable red telephones plugged into ring mains outside cafés and bars. These coin-in-the-slot machines do a roaring trade with rows of Japanese talking excitedly, and continually interrupting themselves with phrases like – do you get me? – am I making myself understood? The Japanese too find their own language complicated and unsatisfactory. The Japanese are as addicted as the British to digging holes in the road but one is immediately impressed by the widespread use of light-weight motor-driven conveyor belts which lead from the bottom of the trench right up to the back of the spoil lorry. There is none of that back-breaking spade swinging which is the mark of the British navvy. One may begin to sense that the Japanese, although they are most energetic, are not given to unnecessary labour. The taxis, for example, have doors which are automatically opened by a pneumatic piston controlled by the driver; the double jointed elbows by which taxi-drivers elsewhere in the world attempt to reach and open their doors have not been evolved in Japan. The portable telephones, the conveyor belts and the taxi door openers are three devices which in retrospect tend to remain in one's memory.

But instead of looking through the visitors' eyes at the cultural sidelights and the memorable trivia of Japan perhaps it would be more appropriate to step back and survey Japan's overall resources with the eye of the geographer.

Japan has a land area (142,000 square miles), just slightly greater than that of Mexico, and her population, at nearly 100 million, is half that of the United States. At the 1960 census the figure was 93,420,000 but the total population has been rising slowly since. Japan ranks seventh in the world in terms of national population after China, India, Russia, the United States, Indonesia and Pakistan. In terms of population density only the Netherlands and Belgium rate above Japan which has 261.5 people to the square kilometre. This figure is, however, misleading because eighty-five per cent of the land area is uninhabited mountainous terrain, and nearly half the population is crowded into only one per cent of the country's total area.

Japan is basically four large islands in an archipelago of thousands of smaller islands and islets. The large islands are Honshu (which contains Tokyo and Osaka), Shikoku, Kyushu, and the northern one Hokkaido. The whole country is volcanic and subject to severe earthquakes since it sits on the circum-Pacific 'ring of fire', a major belt of crustal weakness around the margins of the Pacific Ocean.

The geological map shows that old continental type rock is sparse, and it is in this sort of rock that minerals like tin, lead, zinc, copper and nickel tend to be found. For this reason Japan is obliged to import non-ferrous metals on a large scale. Domestic copper ore, for example, satisfies less than a quarter of total demand. Equally Japan is desperately short of iron ore resources and currently imports ninety-five per cent of her requirements. She does have some coal in Hokkaido and Kyushu but still has to import half the coking coal required for the iron and steel industry. Other raw materials which Japan needs but cannot provide herself are bauxite (100 per cent import), crude oil (100 per cent), raw wool and cotton (100 per cent). The only plentiful mineral resources she does have are limestone and water.

The rainfall varies from 40 to 100 inches. This can only be described as abundant, and since Japan lies in the temperate zone its general appearance from the air is that of green, heavily vegetated mountains diversified by occasional flat green alluvial valleys. Timber is plentiful, agriculture is intensive and hydro-electric power is there for the taking. Forest accounts for sixty per cent of the total land area and wood is a vital raw material in rural areas. It is not only used to build houses but also provides charcoal for heating and cooking too. It is also the basis of the paper industry. As for hydro-electricity, in 1955 it provided for seventy per cent of the country's total consumption. As demand rose and the best sites for dams were progressively used up this proportion fell away and is now down to less than a third of total electricity consumption.

One more thing a geographer would note is that much of the Japanese coastline is bordered by shallow sand banks and mud flats. This factor has encouraged the Japanese to go in for land reclamation on a big scale, and indeed this is frequently the only way of satisfying the intense demand for more land.

The extreme paucity of natural resources is a most important feature of Japan. It has been a tremendous handicap and the story of Japan's economic growth is all the more remarkable because of it. If the Japanese had been able to occupy Australia or Alaska – both full of natural resources – it seems probable that the world would have been able to witness an even more remarkable surge of economic development which would, quite possibly, have put the Japanese people on a par with the United

States by 1980. The quest for raw materials and for room to develop powered Japanese expansion in the thirties and culminated in the idea of the Greater Asian Co-prosperity Sphere. The tremendous defeat suffered at the hands of the Allies in 1945 put an end to these ambitions and Japan is now obliged to live by trade alone at least for the time being.

The odd thing is that nobody really knows where the Japanese people actually came from. They are remarkably homogeneous genetically and are generally supposed to have migrated into the islands at least two thousand years ago. They may have been there in neolithic times. Somebody was but it is not known if these earliest of all settlers were ancestors of the present Japanese. The hairy Ainus are a people of Caucasian origin who are still found in Hokkaido but are slowly dying out. The Japanese are, by contrast, very unhairy and of quite different origin. Among the warring tribes in the first two or three centuries AD a group known as the Yamato Race gradually asserted supremacy and is supposed to have been ancestral to the Japanese Imperial Family.

The tradition of acquiring foreign technology began early with importations of industrial arts from Korea. These included weaving, metal-work, tanning and shipbuilding. The Japanese also have a long tradition of optimising on imported technology and made the best swords in the world in the Middle Ages. Japan, as mentioned, imported the Chinese script and with it some primitive medicine, a calendar, some astronomy and Confucianism. Buddhism also came in from India via China in the sixth century.

The emperors set up court in Kyoto in 794 and inaugurated a period in which the Japanese withdrew into themselves and transformed imported culture and technology into something that could be described as characteristically Japanese. The ruling circles went through the familiar phases of elegance, refinement and decadence, and effective power passed into the hands of feudal military bosses called Shoguns. The feudal knights or samurai practised austerity as a reaction against decadent court manners. Japanese culture balanced its way down the years swaying between hedonism and spartan austerity until the present time. A period of civil war took place at about the same time as the European Renaissance and was brought to an end by another Shogun called Tokugawa. At this point, when Western Europe was reforming so many aspects of society, when the scientific revolution was beginning, and when the foundations for industrialisation were being laid, Japan abruptly turned her back on the West and closed her doors to all contact. Feudalism with its castes – warriors, peasants, artisans and merchants – flourished unchanged until 1868. One remarkable consequence of this is that a Japanese politician of, say, sixty years of age, could well have had a father whose character was formed in an atmosphere akin to that of the thirteenth century in England.

There was a recent example to illustrate the point. A Minister of Transport was obliged to resign after a press uproar about what may well have seemed to him a wholly innocent gesture. As a mark of gratitude to his local political supporters on his appointment, he had ordered express trains to call at the whistle-stop local halt. It was a great and successful lord making a gesture of thanks to his retainers for their loyalty. To judge from the pained and puzzled expression he wore during a subsequent television interview it was obviously a perfectly reasonable thing for him to do; it had only recently become inappropriate.

When the Emperor was re-installed in the Meiji restoration of 1868 the gates of Japan were thrown open to the world after some heavy knocking by Commodore Perry. The Japanese thereupon released their pent-up energies in a desperate effort to catch up with the West, to accomplish in a hundred years what had taken the West a millenium. They set out on a roller-coaster ride of a kind that no other nation has ever experienced. They fought the Russians and won, their militarists usurped democratic rule, they went through a phase of imperial expansion; then came total dictatorship and fascism, then utter defeat, the loss of their empire and occupation by a people they had despised as barbarians.

With General MacArthur the Japanese got all they deserved.

He abolished the Army, Navy and Air Force, hanged the Prime Minister, abolished the state religion and the nobility, burnt the history books and gave women the vote. He confiscated well over a third of the farmland from the absentee landlords and instituted a western style democratic constitution.

After fighting a war under orders to die rather than surrender, after the Kami Kaze suicide attacks on the US Fleet, after the unbelievable defence of Iwo Jima and a dozen other places that have gone down in the chronicle of the world's great battles, the Japanese submitted to the Americans like lambs, but only when their Emperor told them to do so. No wonder Japan is regarded as enigmatic; the whole nation behaved like a hundred-million strong team giving unquestioning loyalty to the leadership in a truly feudal pattern. Although the Japanese absorbed technology and science from the West, they never seem to have absorbed the cultural virtues of dissent, of individualistic rationalism, and old-style feudal ethics still hold sway even in the most modern factory.

Whilst this violent social evolution went on with successive gods, leaders, and values being overturned, the physical environment of the Japanese people was equally tumultuous. Disastrous earthquakes in 1892, 1894 and 1923 razed cities to the ground. The 1923 earthquakes in Tokyo with the accompanying fire killed at least 150,000 people, so did the American fire-bomb raids in the Pacific War. These did as much or even more damage than the two atom bombs dropped on Nagasaki and Hiroshima. At the end of the war about three quarters of Tokyo was levelled with something up to a million houses destroyed or uninhabitable. Forming a yearly base load of disaster, violent typhoons can be relied upon to do tremendous damage with the same regularity as the seasons.

Throughout this century of violent evolution Japan's economy grew steadily and very rapidly. An economy is more than a physical stock of plant and equipment. It must also be understood to include the skill and aptitude of the working people and it is the steady increase of this which partially explains Japan's astounding recovery after the war. From the Meiji restoration onwards Japan's rate of economic growth has been consistently among the highest in the world. It is important to outline this development lest the phrase 'economic miracle' be taken to refer only to a post war phenomenon.

In fact an essential resource, that of an educated people, was being developed even before the Meiji restoration during the declining years of the Tokugawa Shogun's rule. There were specific schools established by the warrior class for their own children and run by central and local governments. There were also thousands of temple schools for ordinary children who were taught reading, writing and arithmetic with the highly flexible Japanese abacus. In addition there was 'daily ethics' founded on Shinto, Buddhism and Confucianism. The teachers came from the priesthood and the lower warrior class, and natural science (it would have been 'natural philosophy' in those days) was conspicuous by its absence, as was any tradition of experimentation. Common people were taught to respect their parents, elder brothers and masters. Service to the master was not paid, but the master was expected to produce gifts. When the Meiji Restoration came the average Japanese was imbued with the virtues of labour, thrift, and faith in those above him in the social hierarchy. This was no prescription for militant trades unionism but on the other hand it was equally unthinkable for masters to display any lack of social responsibility to their workers.

After 1868 the surge of development began under a new leadership that was surprisingly young; most of the men were less than thirty years old. The reforms were political as well as economic. The four caste orders were abolished and the Government stopped paying the warrior class stipends in 1876. Samurai were encouraged into useful occupations and provided with capitalised pension bonds, plus grants for initiating new businesses. The taxation system was also reformed and savings were siphoned away from the agricultural sector for industrial development. This economic take-off was accomplished, India please note, without massive injections of foreign aid. In the Tokugawa period land tax was paid in kind. The new Government decreed that it be paid in money on the basis of the value of the land and that it should not vary with the state of the harvest. Agricultural productivity gains could therefore be kept. From 1870 to 1894 no foreign loan was floated and those issued before 1870, to pay for railroads, were redeemed completely.

The Government set up the cotton industry by importing machinery from Manchester. Other kinds of industry followed. These businesses were then sold off at cheap rates to politically reliable families like Mitsui, Mitsubishi and Asano and from these roots sprang the great Zaibatsu. These were tightly-knit groups of diversified industry and banking interests which became a notorious feature of Japan in the thirties.

After a period of smiling co-operation with Western powers, in which technology was vigorously imported, Japan began to arm itself and developed heavy industry for this purpose. At the same time educational development modelled on the German state system was encouraged. In 1886 the term of compulsory education was established as four years, and eight universities, 250 middle schools and 54,000 elementary schools were set up. The percentage of school attendance was about forty-six per cent in the 1880s and was ninety-seven per cent by 1907. The educational system was utilitarian and developed good workers rather than free-thinking individualists. The combination of German educational philosophy and the Japanese national character went on to produce a legacy of problems for Japan's world neighbours.

After defeating China and Russia in the wars of 1894–5 and 1904–5 and exacting humiliating terms, Japan began to expand, acquiring South Sakhalin, Formosa, Korea and interests in Manchuria. The depression of the 1930s contributed to the weakening of parliamentary government and the Diet became the military extremists' rubber stamp. Between 1868 and 1938 Japan appears to have shown a rate of growth higher than that of any other country in the world. The rate of economic growth has only recently become a political and economic counter of recognised importance, and gross national products are difficult to estimate. Japanese economists have produced some figures (tabulated in the appendix) which appear to show that Japan maintained a four per cent growth rate from 1860 to 1938. This is greater than that for any other country in the world, although the United States maintained 4.3 per cent up to 1913. The European average during this period was around 2.3 with Britain at 2.4. Thereafter the British rate remained stagnant.

It is of course true that high rates of economic growth are probably easier to achieve during take-off if only because of the supply of cheap labour from the agricultural sector. Nevertheless the point must be emphasised that the post-war economic miracle of Japan is no flash in the pan brought about by special circumstances, it is a long standing historical trend extending back at least eighty years. Economic growth in Japan is by now a tradition as deeply rooted as the imperially-based bumbledom and stagnation which distinguishes that other off-shore island, ten thousand miles away on the other side of the Old World. Neither nation is likely to change its ways overnight.

The Pacific War was started by an outstanding example of Japan's inability to understand the complex psychology of liberal democratic Western nations. From the moment the United States battleships heeled over in the watery grave of Pearl Harbour, Japan was destined to be strangled and destroyed. Some historians feel that only such an act could have got the Americans into a war; it was as stark and simple as a Western movie, like shooting a man in the back whilst he was sitting down playing cards and drinking a beer. It had to be avenged and Japan's fate was inevitable.

By the end of the Pacific War the volume of Japan's industrial production was less than thirty per cent of her output in 1936. In the sixty-odd cities which had been subjected to air attack, half the houses were razed to the ground. Tokyo was literally three quarters flattened. The Japanese Navy was at the bottom of the sea and so was most of the merchant marine; only a few coasting vessels remained. There were no exports and no foreign trade, and violent inflation had destroyed all private savings. General MacArthur's first concern, as we have seen, was to hammer democracy into the Japanese psychology; economic revival took second place. The object was to prevent the re-creation of an industrial war-making potential and various measures were taken to strengthen trades unionism and break up the pre-war concentrations of power, the Zaibatsu. Unfortunately, however, as with Germany after the First World War, the policy of economic revenge showed signs of being self-defeating because economic distress was a bad climate in which to foster democratic institutions. Furthermore relief given for straightforward humanitarian reasons began to prove a heavy burden for the United States taxpayer who was already supporting the Marshall Plan in Europe. By 1948 the policies of the Supreme Commander of the Allied Powers (SCAP) were reversed and economic recovery was actively promoted.

Up to the outbreak of the Korean War American aid was running at around 400 million dollars a year. As the Korean War developed, the Japanese economy received the sort of massive boost underdeveloped countries dream of. The United Nations forces used Japan as an arsenal and the United States alone pumped in 2,200 million dollars between 1951 and 1953 in the form of 'special procurement'. This massive injection of foreign currency allowed the Japanese economy to climb to a high growth rate without suffering the braking effects of insoluble balance of payments difficulties, for a critical two or three years. The growth rates (the percentage increase of the previous year's gross national product) for the years 1951, 52, 53 were 12.2, 13.5 and 10.5 per cent. During this period the world's outstanding economic miracle was truly launched and the Japanese government and bureaucracy developed ways of keeping it going. There was a recession in 1954 when the rate fell to 3.3 per cent but in most years it was at least 10 per cent and in 1959 reached a staggering 17.9 per cent. From 1956 onwards gross domestic investment averaged between 30 and 40 per cent of the gross national expenditure. Between 1954 and 1962 the real income per head doubled. To put this in other terms one could say that if a working man did not put in for an annual rise of at least 10 per cent, he would be getting less than his fair share of the national cake, and this is still true.

The constitution of modern Japan remains the same as that introduced by MacArthur in 1947. Some key provisions are that Japan renounces war as a sovereign right and also renounces the threat or the use of force as a means of settling disputes with other nations. The Emperor is a constitutional monarch and does whatever the Government decrees in a way similar to that of the British monarchy. Although, for example, he appoints the Prime Minister and the Chief Justice, these two public servants are themselves designated by the Diet or Japanese Parliament. The Diet has two houses, the House of Representatives and the House of Councillors, and members of both are elected by the Japanese people who are twenty years old and over, on the basis of universal, equal and direct suffrage. The Diet, like Parliament in Britain and Congress in the United States, legislates and determines the national budgets. The executive can be forced to resign by a vote of no confidence in the Diet. Local government runs on the basis of forty-six prefectures which also have elected assemblies. At lower levels there are city, town and village governments.

Defence is interpreted literally in that Japan has no offensive capability such as bomber squadrons or assault ships; at any rate not yet. The cornerstone of the defence policy is the Security Treaty concluded between Japan and the United States in 1951 and amended in 1960. This treaty provides for US military forces to be stationed in Japan as protection against external aggression. There is also a supplementary Mutual Defence Assistance Agreement under which the United States supplies defence equipment. The strength of Japan Self Defence Forces is around 300,000 men. The Maritime Self Defence Force has 40,000 tons worth of ships and the Air Self Defence Force has about 1,000 aircraft including F-104s and Sabres. None of the ships is bigger than a destroyer and none of the fighter aircraft has enough range to do other than defend Japan. Japan's space programme is of course irrelevant in the military context because rockets are of little use without nuclear warheads which Japan does not have.

Japan's total labour force is estimated at nearly 50 million (47,100,000 in the 1964 Labour Census) and nearly a quarter of this force is still employed in agriculture and forestry. Another quarter is employed in manufacturing and the rest are to be found in the distribution system and service industries with 6 per cent each in transport and construction. About 66 per cent of the population works now; this is a slight drop from 1955 when the rate was higher at 70 per cent.

The average Japanese still eats mainly rice, but the consumption of animal foods is steadily increasing. In calories they still constitute only 10 per cent of total intake compared to an average of around 30 per cent in the West. But what the statisticians call non-essential foods are enjoyed to an increasing extent; in a recent four-year period the consumption of whisky doubled (the Japanese Suntory, which is good) and the consumption of beer went up two and half times. Clothing is comparatively cheap and plentiful with personal consumption rising year by year. Only housing remains conspicuously substandard but Japanese women are scrupulously houseproud and the squalor usually associated with poor housing is hard to find. The Government has the slogan 'one house one family' but, with soaring land prices, it has a long way to go.

The Japanese consume communications voraciously; there are over 750 television stations with at least 350 of them devoted to colour. Well over 90 per cent of the Japanese land area is covered. The dominant force is NHK, a public service run as a copy of the BBC but considerably richer because the Japanese are not so mean about paying for licences. It provides an excellent and adult service of both television and radio. The commercial stations are also a sizeable force which keeps NHK on its corporate toes. Newspapers are of high standard with huge circulations. The firms which publish them are rich enough to run private airforces to speed the news and pictures, and journalism is said to be the most exhausting profession in Japan. Competition between reporters is unbelievably frenetic, if not actually violent.

Perhaps it would be as well to end this grasshopper of a chapter in the same way as it began, with a word of advice to the would-be visitor.

First of all if you want to see tourist Japan, submit to the ministrations of Japan's efficient tourist industry. If you try to see ancient shrines and gardens of tranquillity other than on a tour, you may suffer the fate that befell the author who visited an especially soothing garden in Kyoto by taxi. It was not only very much further than the map suggested, it was also closed. A return to the railway station was achieved only by a four-mile walk followed by a two-mile ride on a tram which was so packed that the conductor was literally unable to raise his arm to take the fare. The risk of that sort of experience is not the only reason for going on organised tours either; the fact is that relics of Japan's Meiji past have been tidied away to historical villages whenever they were small enough to move. This even goes for Frank Lloyd Wright's earthquake-proof Imperial Hotel, about the only old building of any distinction in Tokyo. It was saved from complete destruction at the hands of the developers only by an international outcry and it will now moulder away in a far-off museum of tourist 'sights'. If you want to see those bits of old Japan, it is far easier to do so in the tourist bus. It is also the only way you are likely to see inside a Japanese home because there is no tradition of entertaining at home in Japan. Businessmen will gasp at the cost of entertaining clients in Tokyo geisha houses, and they must also realise that geishas are supposed to oil the social wheels of business only.

Japan is of course going Western in every way. Sometimes this is a loss, sometimes it is not. The willingness to grasp the essentials of the Western industrial revolution has brought mixed blessings to the ordinary Japanese in the past. Since the Pacific War, however, a better life has been extended to all the people more rapidly than in any other country in the world, at any time in history. The purpose of this book is to describe some of the things that are going on in this fascinating economic laboratory, so that both poor nations and the stumbling rich ones can learn lessons which, when applied, may extend to many more ordinary people – and the next phrase is written without any cynical overtone – the blessing of a rapidly-rising standard of living.

TWO

Motors: A Modern Industry

Japan manufactures more bicycles and motor cycles than any other country in the world. The next stage in transport evolution is the motor car, and in most major industrial powers the motor industry is the hub of the economy. Up to 1966 it was possible to assert that Japan, oddly enough, had risen to industrial pre-eminence without the benefit of any stimulus from this consumer-orientated industry. At that time an index of industrial advancement, like the size of the steel industry, owed very little to the motor industry. A literal translation of the American economic truism, 'What's good for General Motors is good for the United States' would have been meaningless in Japan, and to some extent this is still true. The top companies in the industrial league tables – Hitachi, Mitsubishi Heavy Industries and Yawata Iron and Steel – are primarily engaged in heavy industry and only indirectly dependent on consumer goods for their earnings. Within the last three years however Japan has plunged right into the motor age and at least two of the big motor companies have become a force in the land. Moreover Japan has become the world's No. 2 automobile manufacturer yielding first place only to the United States.

The problem with leaping so suddenly into the motor age is that motor cars not only have to be manufactured but they have to have somewhere to go. Furthermore people have to get used to them, both as drivers and as pedestrians. Japan is now gripped by what can only be described as motor car fever. A huge road construction programme is in full swing, and urban fly-overs are going up like mushrooms to ease a congestion which is as good, or as bad, as anything that London, Paris or New York can offer. Where the traffic does move freely the scene is still more remarkable. With so many new drivers, Japan has the highest accident rate in the world. Any Western visitor is warned off attempting to hire a self-drive car – it would be very hazardous even if he could read the road signs. However, a trip in a Japanese taxi is at least as frightening; exultant drivers, armed in new chrome, thrust and swing at each other, testing reflexes, clutches and brakes to the utmost. Belgian drivers are disciplined and predictable by comparison. Phrases like Sedan Samurai or Kami Kaze driver give some indication of the atmosphere. In many streets in Tokyo, pedestrians wishing to cross the road seize yellow flags kept in bins on lamp standards, hold them aloft and step out with the uncertain tread of soldiers holding up the white flag to a treacherous enemy. This is quite understandable for death is not far away. At least thirteen thousand pedestrians are killed every year, a number that goes on rising.

Japan's status in the world league tables of vehicle production has been comparatively high for some time but until recently this was due simply to a very large output of trucks. Ten years ago, for example, she held eighth place in the world hierarchy and over 80 per cent of the vehicles produced were trucks. This situation has been completely reversed and in 1967 a typical month's production for the largest manufacturer, Toyota, was something like this: 81,000 vehicles total output, 800 buses, 2,000 heavy trucks, 32,000 station wagons and light trucks, 42,000 passenger cars. As little as five years before those proportions were in the reverse order.

The relative rates of growth of the various sectors tell the real story. Over the recent ten-year period, bus output doubled, truck output rose twenty-fold and passenger cars forty-fold. Various intermediate classes of vehicles are in evidence. There is, for example, a fashion for vans and small trucks which offer passenger car comfort at least in the driving cab. These vehicles can be used for both business and pleasure. In the post-war period the three-wheeled truck, primarily identified with the 'Mazda' trade mark, was widespread and in 1963 it accounted for over a third of all motor vehicles, other than motor cycles. It is now on the way out in the home market, although as Japan's transport history is recapitulated in the developing countries of South East Asia, the three-wheeled truck is a thriving export business. In Japan heaviest sales are in very small cars but preference is now shifting to cars bigger than 1,000 c.c. capacity.

In the 1950s many Japanese car firms entered into licence agreements with foreign firms in an effort to close the technological gap engendered by the Allied Occupation. Nissan tied up with BMC, Isuzu with Rootes, and Hino with Renault. Even today many of these last-generation British and French designs are still seen on the roads. (The Japanese, as already mentioned, are as perverse as the British and the Indians in that they still drive on the left.)

In the last three or four years however Japanese manufacturers have brought out their own designs, many of which sport absurd names. One common sight is a Nissan car called the 'Cedric' and another is the 'Mazda'. Such names which evoke theatrical green-room gossip and well-known light bulbs do little to help export prospects. But the Japanese feel that eventually, their cars will sell abroad on price and merit. Although the Emperor has three Rolls Royces, Prince Motors was encouraged to provide something of similar calibre in Japanese style. Whether it can equal that palladian aristocratic grace remains to be seen, for style is something Japanese cars have rather lacked. Recently an Italian designer was imported to produce a large high-class car for one well-known company. So many Japanese designers contributed their ideas as well that the result looks fussy, huddled, and far from Italian. Many of the older designs of Japanese car look rather solid and chunky but the more recent models like Toyota's Corolla and Toyo Kogyo's Mazda 1500 at long last do have a distinctive and graceful air.

What are the influences which demand that the Japanese car

should be the sort of machine it is? One of them, the samurai strain in the Japanese national character, has already been mentioned. Cars which do not accelerate vividly and respond quickly are unlikely to be popular and there is no sign of that lingering yearning for the vintage aristocratic carriage that distinguishes British or Italian taste. There are few echos of the walnut fascia or that chauffeur-driven, 'real leather' air which used to mark the Lancia or the Armstrong-Siddeley. Such refinements may well have a market value in the future as any Japanese who has swished through the clamour of Tokyo in the silent and lofty luxury of a Rolls Royce will admit. Nevertheless the current virtues of Japanese cars are purposeful solidity and it is worth spending a moment in discussing Japanese roads because these have been the major formative influence.

Until three or four years ago Japanese roads were poor. The national highways, like the urban streets, were made for feet and were marked out in feudal times. Trails in the mountains were particularly labyrinthine and there was no Roman tradition of straight military roads, as in Continental Europe and Great Britain. Few people dared risk a long car journey because it usually turned into a sort of motorised assault course with endless potholes of uncertain depth interspersed with mud slides or, in dry weather, belts of dust so thick that headlights were needed. A car to cope with this had to be, if nothing else, very solid. One such machine was Toyota's Crown, a vehicle whose indestructibility also made it a favourite with taxi firms in the cities.

Japan's economic planners dictated that, by the 1964 Olympic Games, Japan had better have some good roads, at least in the cities. In Tokyo there are urban motorways built on stilts that are more extensive than in any city outside the United States. These are toll motorways costing over three shillings a trip and official thinking holds that toll roads are the only way to a speedy and adequate road construction programme. Motorways being built between towns, like the one joining Kobe Osaka and Nagoya, are owned by public corporations which envisage charging tolls for the next 30 or 40 years. Inside Tokyo, urban motorway should amount to 80 miles by 1972. The country as a whole should have 780 miles by the same date.

The actual planned expenditure is so large that money has been scooped from everywhere – even the World Bank. £53,000 million is expected to be spent by 1985 when the planners expect 30 million vehicles on the road. In 1966 the total was a mere eight million vehicles.

The work on the ordinary road-widening and surfacing programmes tends to be done by agricultural labour taken from near by. One of the most bizarre sights is the Japanese version of that familiar road construction worker whose responsibility is to direct the traffic with a red and green flag and make tea for his workmates. In Japan this is as likely as not to be a village woman wearing a glass fibre helmet on top of a traditional straw hat with a flag in one hand and a walkie-talkie radio in the other.

All this has meant that in the past cars tended to be either big and very solid or very small and used only inside towns. The two best examples of this were probably the Toyota Crown and the tiny Toyo Kogyo Mazda 360. The popularity of this latter car with an engine no bigger than a medium-sized motor cycle, also rested on the fact that the registration was very cheap and the driving licence easy to get, since there was no need to pass a written examination.

Over the last few years cars have evolved away from these two extremes preserving only the older virtue of solidity. Mazda cars have increased in engine capacity up to 1,500 c.c. and Toyotas have also gravitated to the 1,100 c.c. – 1,500 c.c. range with the latest, the Corolla, already a best-seller.Toyota in 1967 ranked as the seventh largest auto manufacturer in the world with only Fiat, Volkswagen and Renault set above it outside the United States. In total production it is just ahead of Nissan though the latter is not nearly so strong in passenger cars.

Toyota started as an offshoot of Toyoda Automatic Loom in 1933 but very nearly went bankrupt in 1947. The company was helped by Mitsui Bank whose Osaka office Director, Fukio Nakagawa, became Toyota's managing director in 1950. Under his direction the company grew rapidly and demonstrated that paternalism so characteristic of the larger Japanese firms. Toyota City grew up to be, literally, a company town where workers get company houses and free transport to their place of work. They get a free health service. Food, clothing and holidays come cheaper and they can buy a Toyota car at a very low price. Their purchasing power is probably greater than that of any other workers in Japan and is at least as good as that of their counterparts in Britain or France. Only the undermanagers get comparatively poorly paid – but they at least have the status symbols of special armbands and badges.

Toyota's first export success came with the Land Cruiser. This is a rugged cross-country vehicle slightly larger than, but otherwise very similar to, the Land Rover. Most observers would have thought that the British company's grip on the world market was unshakeable but the Japanese proceeded to launch their product in, of all places, Australia.

They were fortunate in picking a good distributor and fortunate too in that memories of the Pacific War had begun to fade. The Land Cruiser had a big six-cylinder engine and this gave it a slight edge in performance over the original four-cylinder Land Rover, particularly in heavy sand. The British company was slow to respond to the challenge from the machine and equally slow to meet the challenge of aggressive salesmanship. Soon the usual Japanese figures of surging exports were being relayed, not only from Australia but from Africa and even South East Asia.

There is nothing special or new about Toyota's cars. There are minor things like transparent reservoirs for hydraulic fluid so that inspection is easy, and an accessible clutch adjustment by the bonnet rim that could be operated even by a girl in evening dress, but there are no exotic suspension systems or air-cooled engines. Like most other Japanese cars, they are simple and straightforward.

The Japanese motor industry has structural problems which it must put right soon. The 35–40 per cent tariff barrier, which keeps out imports, and the policies that exclude foreign capital will not last for ever, and by the time trade liberalisation comes the indigenous motor companies must be big enough to stand alone. At present there are simply too many companies. The largest, Toyota, is the size BMH was before the merger with Leyland, and most companies are small by British standards. The Government encourages mergers in a variety of ways. One of them is said to involve meetings of unimaginable length which go on for months until the parties are bored into exploring the possibilities of amalgamation. The industry currently employs over half a million workers but there are at least ten major firms and many minor ones.

The pattern of manufacture is different from that in the European and American industries in that chassis manufacturers dominate and frequently incorporate their parts suppliers. Many companies pride themselves on making nearly all the parts for their own cars. This is one factor which makes amalgamation difficult. Another obstacle is the existence of plant unions. These are unions which embrace all skills based within one particular plant, in contrast to craft unions which embrace all men with one particular skill (such as boilermakers) on a national basis.

When Nissan and Prince amalgamated they were greatly troubled by the need to amalgamate their labour unions. Recently Toyota and Hino (a famous truck manufacturer) negotiated a tie-up rather than an outright merger and are expected to put the initial emphasis on co-ordinated sales and the adjustment of models. Nissan and Prince had command of thirty per cent of the auto market this year and the combined shares of Toyota and Hino were around forty per cent. The progress of amalgamation is therefore well advanced and the growth of the two major companies will help it along.

It would be wrong to give the impression that the advance of the Japanese industry will depend exclusively on the creation of larger economic units producing only conventional cars. There are for example two major companies in Japan which do have a very high reputation for innovation. These are Honda and Toyo Kogyo. Their success may come to depend heavily on their inventive powers because Toyota and Nissan between them have already got over seventy per cent of the passenger car market.

First Honda. In comparison with Toyo Kogyo the company is small beer and has but a tiny proportion of the home market. Nevertheless it has huge resources founded on the motor cycle business and may soon be a force to be reckoned with. Honda is unconventional in many ways; the company will not operate through trading companies abroad for example. Furthermore most of its products have some extraordinary mechanical feature. The N 360 small car has an air-cooled, parallel twin-cylinder engine that runs at a speed of over 8,500 revolutions per minute! However the most interesting technical feature involves the use of plastics.

A plastic motor car offers the possibility of being lighter in weight and rustless. For the manufacturer it means that the same engine should give a higher performance to the car and it also means the end of the wearisome paint shop. It should mean a dramatic reduction in fabrication costs too, because complex shapes can be moulded in one shot instead of being laboriously assembled by welding together steel pressings. In general the world's motor manufacturers have been slow to try plastics in spite of the fact that when the comparison is made between panels of equal stiffness polypropylene is as cheap as steel. It should be added that the attractions of plastics lie in injection-moulded thermoplastics which can be mass-produced, not in hand-lay-up glass fibre technology or the slow business of vacuum forming.

Honda has gone far beyond the usual applications for fascias and rear seat mouldings. The rear boot lid is injection-moulded thermoplastic and in Japan door panels and wings of ABS plastic or polypropylene are in use. These are self-coloured to match the other parts of the car which are still metal. Honda has also made a wider use of plastic hinges for such parts as the glove-pocket and lid. What the future holds is, as yet, unclear, but it is known that the factory has installed very large injection-moulding machines capable of exerting the necessary high locking pressures.

The effect of these technical developments on Honda's prospects should be reflected in car prices. Toyo Kogyo however has decided to aim for the heights by backing a completely new kind of engine. Toyo Kogyo is one of the best companies to examine for some view of the technological capability of the Japanese industry. In Japan it is famous for being computer crazy and, of course, for having the technological courage to try to make the rotary piston engine into a commercial proposition.

The Toyo Kogyo company is based entirely in Hiroshima, on the east side of the town where a large river runs into the sea. It survived the atom bomb, being protected from the blast by a hill. In wartime days the company only made three-wheeled trucks, rifles and machine tools. This three-wheeled truck is a Japanese speciality understandable only when one sees the tiny narrow back streets of the old towns. Its manoeuvrability and fuel economy made it immensely popular, and between 1931 when production began and 1957, Toyo Kogyo made 200,000 of them. But as Japan got richer the markets shifted, four-wheeled trucks came into fashion and so did cars. Due to the licensing regulations, the unimaginably tiny car with the 360 c.c. engine came to constitute a sizeable market opportunity which Toyo Kogyo seized with both hands in 1960. Once in the passenger car field the company grew rapidly, raising its capital from £8 million to £25 million in five years. Now it makes larger cars up to 1,500 c.c. and has launched a sports car called the Cosmo, powered by a 1,000 c.c. Wankel NSU rotary piston engine. This has come at an opportune time as Japan's network of expressways under construction will at last give a fast sports car somewhere to go.

Fierce competition among car makers in Japan has led to the manufacture of a large number of rapidly changing models. With small production runs, this kind of thing can be ruinously uneconomic. Toyo Kogyo set about the problem by calling in IBM and applying full computer control to its five production lines. Now computers select the production stock and deliver at the right place and at the right time the correct parts for anything from 360 c.c. light cars to a two-litre truck. Any production line can therefore carry any kind of vehicle with the whole thing humming along as if it were a conventional line devoted to only one standard model. In this way Toyo Kogyo can handle up to thirty-seven different models, some with engines at the rear, some with engines in front and all in many different colours, as if they constituted a normal mass-production flow. This pattern has now been widely copied, notably by Toyota.

With a flow of thirty thousand cars a month, which is small by European standards, this is a vital economy. Many of the machine tools are tape-controlled and computers are used extensively in the design of components like cams and gears. In all, eleven computers are at work, not only on plant operation control but on pay-roll, inventory, market research and basic cost calculations. In 1966 the company announced that its sales network was also to be computer based – with remote sales and service points continuously feeding in data by telelink. IBM 1050 terminals are linked to a 360 computer at Head Office in Hiroshima. The computer memorises necessary information such as the total stock in store, and, when asked, checks the incoming data against total stock and issues the necessary instructions for shipment. Information obtained from the computer is also fed back to the sales network to help in sales analyses. Lastly the computer orders the works to produce parts to restore the stock to its original optimum level.

The men in command of this company are all engineers from the president, Tsuneji Matsuda, downwards. This may account for their fascination with computers and engineering techniques. It certainly accounts for the NSU Wankel engine development. In 1960, when Toyo Kogyo went into passenger cars, Matsuda went to Germany and obtained the Japanese licence. Since then intensive development work has gone on resulting in a 1,000 c.c. (100 h.p.) sports car. In the rotary piston engine (the name of the German inventor was Wankel) the piston does not move up and down in a cylinder. Instead a specially shaped block of metal (the piston) rests inside a cylinder touching the walls at three points. A fuel and air mixture is detonated in one of the three spaces and the expanding gases rotate the piston bringing the next space in line with the fuel inlet and so on. The attractions of the rotary piston engine are many. For one thing the volume of the engine per horsepower is less than half that required for ordinary piston and crankshaft engines. The saving in space and weight, however, is no more important than the surprising reduction in moving parts and vibration. There are no more valves, springs, cams or reciprocating pistons – yet the power output passes through a conventional clutch and gearbox.

The novelty of the engine is not so much a barrier to its introduction as the much greater novelty of the gas turbine. The Cosmo sports car is capable of 100 m.p.h. and gives one the feeling of vivid acceleration which comes from a car with twice the engine capacity. It came on to the market at a very competitive price. The problems which have always had to be solved in such an engine are primarily those of sealing the piston as its three corners scrape the inside of the cylinder. If Toyo Kogyo has solved these problems successfully, it is on to a very good thing. Not only will the engine be cheaper, but its power can be raised merely by stacking the cylinders on the same shaft. The current engine is a two-piston (each sweeping 500 c.c.) version which has run 100,000 kms. continuously on the test track. World competitors with the exception of Germany's NSU appear dormant and in any case are unlikely to compete in the small cheap car class since they include Rolls Royce, Porsche and Alfa Romeo.

The rotary engine and the wide use of computers indicate considerable engineering courage. Toyo Kogyo, perhaps for reasons connected with engineering purism, also makes about a third of its own machine tools, including transfer machines. It forges its own crankshafts and half shafts, casts its own iron from cupola blast furnaces and uses shell-moulding techniques with its own resin-bonded sands. It also sells the output of its machine tool plant separately, though the sale of tools, gauge blocks, rock drills (a traditional speciality pre-dating car manufacture) and coated sands accounts for only four per cent of the firm's total sales. In the field of rock drills, however, its total market share is nearly fifty per cent. The only things they cannot make, its managers say with pride, are the tyres, the wind-screens, the seals and the wide strip steel sheet for the bodies. A last surprising touch is the means of delivery of its cars. Rather than trust them to Japanese railways or drive them to their destinations over Japan's still inadequate roads, the company delivers them by sea – in fifty-seven of its own ships. 'Mazda Line' ships berth alongside the factory loading the cars direct from the assembly lines.

One interesting feature is the company's attitude to exports. During the home market credit squeeze in 1964 and 1965, Toyo Kogyo doubled its exports – so that in spite of contraction at home net sales stayed the same. Why don't other car producers like the British do the same? Of course it is less profitable to sell abroad but when asked if the shareholders objected, Executive Director Murao seemed not to understand the question. 'Everyone in Japan knows we must export above all else,' he said. 'Exports are good for Japan though not perhaps directly for the shareholders.' The shareholders may not mind either way because Toyo Kogyo's profitability is among the highest in Japan – and its net income gets it fifth place of all companies in Japan.

One thing about the Japanese motor industry is clear: although it still relies on some imported know-how it is rapidly developing a technological character of its own. As the industry grows this will be a source of strength as important as its huge home market.

THREE

Shipbuilder to the World

The world has grown familiar with Japan as the Number One shipbuilder. The strains of 'Rule Britannia' have long since died away on the wind, and the ubiquitous Liberty ships once the miracle of the American shipyards though a British design are but a rusty recollection of another proud industry now in decline. Not only is Japan the largest shipbuilder of any nation in the world, she builds what are individually the largest ships and will soon build more ships than the rest of the world put together. To tidy up the whole scene she will soon be the largest ship owner as well, or so the Japanese themselves confidently predict.

Given this abundance of superlatives it is fairly difficult to catch the eye of the passing observer of the shipping scene with something new. Even the stunning colour photographs of shipyard activity, which are always taken on days when the weather has an alpine brilliance (they can never compete on the Clyde or the Baltic), are a stale and accustomed sight.

But perhaps this will raise an eyebrow. Remember first the scene on the Clyde when the latest Cunarder, the 55,000 ton Queen Elizabeth 2 slid down the slipway, into the constricted waters of the Clyde. As the television commentators reminded the audience, already uneasily aware that John Brown's shipyard had no more orders, the same traditional slipway had seen the birth of the Queen Mary back in 1931. This was a matter for sentimental pride, as interviews with a few old workers who had riveted the flanks of earlier Atlantic greyhounds were meant to indicate.

Contrast this scene with what is due to be opened at Tsu, Mie Prefecture, for Nippon Kokkan by 1970. A new building dock is to be constructed and it will be capable of taking a 500,000 ton dwt. tanker. The new shipyard will cost twenty million pounds and should produce annual sales of about thirty million pounds. There will be no old-fashioned wooden wedges, tallow slides and tons of old chain to accompany the launching of a new ship. Instead the dock will be flooded up and the ship floated out. The interesting thing, however, is that the dock will have an entrance at each end and a movable gate in the middle. A 500,000 ton tanker would occupy the whole dock, of course, but if two smaller ships were built, there would be no need, as on a slipway, to ensure that the seaward one was completed first. Furthermore it would be possible to start, say, a 300,000 ton dwt. tanker and a 150,000 ton dwt. bulk carrier at the same time. The after end of the bulk carrier would include machinery and bridge sections and this would be isolated from the tanker by the movable door. The tanker finished first would be launched through, say, the north entrance, and after pumping out the dock, the movable door would be shifted to allow the bulk carrier to be completed; meanwhile another ship could be started near the northern entrance. Eventually the bulk carrier would be launched through the south entrance. The process would then be repeated, moving the door to allow the third ship to be finished.

The advantages that this provides over a slipway are obviously great gains in flexibility and the opportunity to employ the equipment and space of the yard to the maximum. Furthermore there is increasing worry about damage to really large ships when they are launched from conventional slips. A building dock with one entrance can be operated to build two ships at once but only by moving a half-completed ship. Nippon Kokkan's new yard will save the time and money required to do this and will therefore be marginally more efficient than a conventional building dock, and much more efficient than a slipway.

This example serves to illustrate the determination of Japanese shipbuilders to achieve the utmost efficiency by any method to hand. This determination is to be found not just in major capital investments but in the most minute detail of shipbuilding practice. The Japanese would find nothing to shout about in launching a state-supported white elephant down a slipway fifty years old.

It is tempting to see the success of the shipbuilding industry as a classic example of the way Japan is often supposed to have risen to industrial eminence. The basic reason could be the ample supply of cheap and willing labour quite happy to work long hours in the open air, labour that has not been softened by prosperity and made unco-operative by trade unionism. Indeed, the sight of workers arriving early and doing physical training exercises before the day's work appears to confirm one's worst fears. Some observers have however, reported signs of the British disease, workers who ignore the forceful bellow of the loudspeakers and lounge about smoking a last cigarette before collecting their tools. The car parks are already full of workers' new cars. Maybe the good days are over, and indeed employers complain that wages are as high as in Western Germany, and that good labour is now in short supply because everyone prefers lighter, cleaner work. Masashi Isano, president of the Shipbuilders' Association of Japan, warns that 'our shipbuilding industry is now confronted with the same problems as those which have beset the West European shipbuilding nations'. These problems will not, however, include the profound traditionalism of both unions and managements which has dragged down the European industries and imposed heavy restraints on the Americans. As will become clear, Japan's success depends more on modern management techniques than on willing workers and paradoxically they have the Americans to thank for it.

Looking back to, say, 1954, it seems incredible that the Japanese should have chosen to throw their industrial weight into shipbuilding. At that time the world was full of wartime Liberty and Enterprise ships which had been churned out by American yards with a speed and regularity which belonged more to the mass-production lines of the motor industry than to traditional shipbuilding. Furthermore the great shipbuilding nations of Western Europe were building up production again. There were other problems too. For example, the Japanese steel industry was in poor shape, producing expensive and inferior plate for which ninety per cent of the raw materials had to be imported.

There were three factors which provoked some degree of optimism. After the war not only was Japan denied a ship-building industry by the Americans but aviation and atomic energy developments were banned as well. Consequently there was a fairly large and unharnessed army of high-grade scientific and engineering talents looking for something to do. Secondly, American control over shipbuilding was relaxed just in time for the boom in world shipping set off by the Korean war, and at the same time Japan began trying to rebuild at least her pre-war tonnage of ocean-going ships. Thirdly, an American business-man, Mr. K. Ludwig, had leased the Kure shipyard to build ships for his National Bulk Carrier Corporation. He calculated that with Japanese talent and Japanese low wages he could build his own ships at least as economically there as anywhere else. Moreover with American production techniques National Bulk Carrier was likely to get a very good bargain indeed! Japanese shipyards were therefore supplied with high-grade engineering talent, growing demand, and the shining example of the best American production techniques at Kure. These three factors, together with determined management, Government support and some very good luck, put the Japanese ship-building industry ahead of the world in 1956 and it has stayed there ever since.

The traditional way of building ships is very easy to understand. In fact it is the way that first comes to the mind of any practical man who does not know much about modern ship-building. Obviously the keel is laid first because this is the heaviest, strongest and most cumbersome section of the ship. The keel also has to be straight because if it is not, the ship's hydrodynamic performance will be grossly affected and all sorts of corrective action may be necessary. So, traditionally, ship-builders got the keel right first. Then the ribs and strakes were built up and clad with steel plates usually starting at the bows and working towards the stern which would enter the water first at the launch. Until a few years ago Clyde shipbuilders even began tankers at the bows and worked down aft. One obvious effect of this practice was that the workers concerned with fitting pipes, electrical conduit, doors, ventilation systems and upper-deck rigging such as derricks and winches, simply had nothing to do unless another ship near by was in the later stages of building. Even when there was enough work in the yards the flow of this particular work was subject to large variations. With a tanker the practice was ludicrous because all the compli-cations are in the stern sections which contain the engine room, crews' quarters, bridge, lifeboats and electrical generation equip-ment. Consequently after weeks of welding up acres of bare plate, the work schedule would demand an absolute rush of finishing effort. With one of those traditional who-bores-the-holes-in-this disputes thrown in, any hope of delivery on time was in the lap of the gods. Furthermore, the unforeseen delays which usually occur in finishing have their maximum impact with these traditional styles of building. Responsibility for the work usually rests with the gang foreman. This man not only runs the gang but functions as the time keeper and the controller of the quantity of materials used. He provides the information on which middle management operates. Most of the skill and a great deal of the responsibility in traditional shipbuilding there-fore lies on the shop floor under the command of the 'hard hat' – a name given to the foreman because of the tradition of wearing a bowler hat as a mark of authority – and, some cynics say, as protection from carelessly dropped tools.

All this was simply not good enough for the Japanese.

In 1952 a study group was set up to work out a system of production control. It attempted to fuse experience gained by experts from the former Japanese Navy with the Liberty ship style 'sequential work units' introduced by F. L. Hann of the American National Bulk Carrier Corporation; further contributions came from members of the still defunct aircraft industry, particularly the technique of arranging fabrication drawings into the best order for mass production.

During this period the National Bulk Carrier Corporation, which had leased the Kure Dockyard, was building a 38,000 ton tanker, one of the biggest in the world at the time. Japanese eyes were focused on this yard not only because it was building very big ships (an 85,000 tonner was launched in 1956) but because these ships were being built in a way wholly at variance with tradition. At Kure, design and management staff spent much more time on thinking about 'how to build' than on 'what to build'.

The modern pattern which finally evolved starts with production designing. The aim of this is to split the construction process into unit jobs and to issue specific instructions on how to perform each job and the exact sequence to be followed. Since these are quantified in terms of man hours, any falling behind schedule will be spotted very quickly because it will have happened in a small segment of the construction process. After the process is split into unit jobs, sub-assembly begins in a covered factory. In these improved conditions men work better and so do machines. Welding in particular is more efficient under cover. The sub-assembly units can be planned so as to minimise welding in awkward positions. Sub-assembly can thus be regarded as pre-fabrication.

The next stage, the assembly, also goes on under cover and sections of the ship weighing up to six hundred tons each are put together and completed as far as possible. This is the critical stage and the overall productivity of the entire shipyard depends on it. Accordingly, vigorous efforts have gone into rationalising this stage. Separate production lines have been established for those assemblies which are mainly boxlike compartments, for those which are mainly curved bits like the double bottoms and bow sections and for those which support parts of the upper deck with bollards and winches. Assembly methods which best suit the kind of work can therefore be applied consistently and workers do not have to switch from such jobs as fitting curved plates together for the stern, to fitting flat strengthening plates to support upper deck winches. Jobs are more routine but they are also done more efficiently. The gang foreman is free to concentrate on supervising the quality of the work done and the men themselves are engaged in largely repetitive and standardised work. On the other hand the most expert workers are employed all the time in doing the things which actually require their skill. Plumbing for example is concentrated in automated pipe shops where the assembly units are fitted out with all the pumps and valves they require. Connecting them up to the adjacent compartment will be left for less skilled workers to do later on. Testing the fitted-up components is yet another stage to be completed at a specific time by the skilled tradesmen.

In this atmosphere it becomes much easier to pick out the kind of activity that really costs money and in which it is worthwhile investing research effort. An example of this was the recently successful drive to develop automatic one-side-only welding.

Only now does attention switch to what used to be the hub of classic shipbuilding, the actual building berth itself, outside in the open air. The Japanese regard these as expensive pieces of capital equipment (very true for the dry-dock building berths) which have to be worked very hard to amortize their cost. The prefabrication techniques have gone so far now that a modern building berth may have only one or two major cranes capable of lifting 200 or even 300 tons each (600 tons together) served by ground-level conveyor belts. These conveyor belts, by the way, are also a feature of the assembly and sub-assembly shops. All that remains to be done in the building berths is to weld the sections together. 'The key factors governing the efficiency of the erection stage are', says Hisashi Shinto of IHI, very tersely, 'the density of work input at the assembly joints, the welding speed, the dimensional accuracy of the assemblies supplied, and the precision of the welded joints.' Those are the remarks of a man who knows not only what *he* is doing, but also what everybody else is *supposed* to be doing. His company, Ishikawajima-

Harima built what was for a long time the world's largest ship, the 209,000 ton tanker Idemitsu Maru.

How much do Japanese workers get paid for labouring under the eagle eyes of graduate engineers fanatically shaving minutes and yen off the man hours and costs wherever they can? As a generalisation the Japanese are fond of saying that, on the basis of purchasing power, their wage level already exceeds that of France and Italy and is up to West German standards. Since devaluation it should be well ahead of British standards. One example, attributed to IHI, suggests that a welder in his middle thirties with eleven years' experience will get over a thousand pounds per annum excluding the company fringe benefits. However, the smaller companies involved in shipbuilding pay up to fifty per cent less than the giants and these companies do a great deal of work for them under sub-contract. This does not mean, incidentally, that their workers escape the rigours of production control; their relationship to the big companies is far closer than is the case in Britain or Germany and they have to dance to the tune of the head piper.

Japanese shipyards also tend to pay less for their steel. Partly this is due to the efficiency of the Japanese steel industry, and partly to the fact that steel plants are often adjacent to shipyards and owned by the same company. Nippon Kokkan is one of the best examples.

How do Japanese ships compare to European ones in price? That's not an easy question to answer because shipowners like to make out that the difference is up to twenty per cent whereas the Japanese Ship Association, trying to avoid stimulating the opposition, likes to say that it's only seven or eight per cent. Whatever the price differential the Japanese have not given their ships away. They have made very big profits in recent years and they have reinvested them wisely. 171 million pounds was ploughed back between 1958 and 1965 of which nearly twenty per cent has gone on new docks and building berths. An even larger proportion has gone into assembly equipment, conveyors and cranes. Five or six entirely new yards appeared between 1964 and 1968 all capable of building 300,000 ton ships. It looks as if Japan will still have little effective competition in the 'big ships' zone so that profit margins may remain high. At least six 300,000 ton tankers are already on order and the inexorable laws of transport economics will ensure that the demand for big ships stays high.

Although Japanese shipbuilding got its world lead by building big simple tankers and ore carriers with National Bulk Carrier in the lead until as late as 1959, the industry has now turned to more complex ships like dry cargo liners and container ships. Just as in the aircraft industry there is a Dakota replacement market, so in shipping, there is thought to be a Liberty ship replacement market. Several shipbuilders around the world have their eye on this, and the British firm Austin and Pickersgill has already produced a very successful standard ship selling for about a million pounds. One of the most successful competing Japanese designs is again from IHI, the 'Freedom' class of which over fifty had been ordered by late 1967. Hitachi, a sprawling group which appears to account for over 2 per cent of Japan's gross national product, has produced a fine container ship with a high degree of automation. As in many British and continental ships during night watches at sea the engine room will be unmanned and controlled from a machinery observation centre by only one watchkeeper. This is as much a tribute to machinery makers as to the automation designers.

Nevertheless Japanese shipbuilders have done their sums and they predict that the greater tonnage needs in the early seventies will still be for tankers and bulk carriers. In this sector they are likely to stay top. Smoothly their spokesmen say that it is not their intention to increase their share of the world's shipbuilding orders but they would like to maintain 'reasonable profit margins by avoiding excessive competition'.

Their competitors are, of course, West European shipbuilders backed by government support of a generosity that has rocked the Japanese. Even giants like Mitsui, Mitsubishi and Hitachi are unable to ignore the effect of direct twenty per cent investment grants and almost unlimited credit like that provided by the British.

To describe the Japanese shipbuilding industry's success in terms of technology, although it makes the whole thing sound simple and comprehensible, really presents a very distorted account of what is after all an interaction of men, money, machines and luck. The technology applied has been utterly essential and in the last analysis the most excellent financial management, labour relations and salesmanship would have been utterly wasted without it. But before leaving the subject perhaps it would be as well to mention some important background factors concerning men, money and luck.

Firstly, the Japanese shipbuilding industry has about 5,000 university graduates with degrees in naval architecture working at all levels of management. In Japan it is a glamour industry for scientists and engineers, and fifteen years ago it was even more glamorous because there was no aviation industry or atomic energy development to lure them aside. Furthermore, some of the best men from the Japanese wartime aviation industry had taken jobs in shipbuilding because there was nowhere else to go, except possibly railway engineering. These men were able to get through to management, either because management, being Japanese, was keen to copy advanced techniques or because the expansion of the industry gave opportunities for engineers and scientists to get into new jobs in planning and management.

This latter process of expansion may be attributed to luck, Colonel Nasser, and the intelligent intervention of the Japanese Government. The Korean war provided the first impetus, which was happily augmented by the needs of Japan's own expanding economy. Just as this cycle had worked itself out, the Suez crisis not only increased the world demand for ships but reminded everybody that if the ship was big enough, going round the Cape of Good Hope was not necessarily more expensive than going through the Canal. It was in 1956 that Japan displaced Britain from the top of the league even though it is admitted that Japan was not internationally competitive at the time. However, the steel industry was doing better and the Government stepped in with low-interest loans and credit.

At this point the industry's management clung closely to the idea of co-operation with government, academic and steel industry research circles. Even so, 1957 was a crisis year with a worldwide fall in orders. Here again luck helped because the Japanese domestic economy now began to boom. Japanese domestic transport relies heavily on coastal shipping but it was not from this source that the shipbuilding firms got their cash flow. It was from chemical plant, civil engineering, construction machinery and pipe lines for use inside Japan. If the shipbuilding firms had previously entertained doubts about the advisability of having their fingers in too many pies, this experience dispelled them for good. Even in 1956 shipbuilding and repairs accounted for no more than sixty-three per cent of the total business and by 1965 it had declined to forty-six per cent.

From the late fifties onwards the industry took care of itself.

Currently it is merging various members to make stronger groups and planning a higher degree of automation in anticipation of a labour shortage. West European competitors have at long last woken up to the truth, which is simply that Japanese shipbuilders are better. To catch up will cost a revolution in management and union behaviour, and a great deal of government money.

FOUR

Aircraft: An Industry Revived

General Douglas MacArthur abolished the Japanese aircraft industry on 18 November 1945. With his imperial word, an industry that employed a million people was dispersed, Japanese government or semi-government bodies were henceforth prohibited from engaging in anything to do with aviation without the express permission of the Supreme Commander Allied Powers (SCAP) and the designers of such famous aircraft as the Zero fighter moved out into other fields. Some went to shipbuilding or automobile engineering, some went to university teaching and, rumour has it, at least one became a nightclub entertainer.

The development of Japanese aircraft ceased in the era of doped fabric, tail wheels and piston engines. Such features as tricycle undercarriages, jet engines and pressurised cabins which came to distinguish new civil aircraft in the West, to say nothing of supersonic flight for military aircraft, were all fully developed while the Japanese aviation industry did not officially exist. Furthermore the cost of developing new aircraft went on rising and the ability of anyone to compete with the American industry went on declining. Yet, at a time when the British were beginning to feel that their own comparatively successful aircraft industry was too expensive to maintain against the competition and that it might as well be wound up, the Japanese decided to start again from scratch, with at least ten years of development to make good.

The spectacle of Japan wilfully setting out on the road to ruin was therefore particularly interesting, and the British, in the shape of a delegation from the Society of British Aerospace Companies, went along in 1967 to have a closer look. Their conclusion was that the Japanese were quite determined to have an aircraft industry and that the motive was basically national pride. A close look at the way the Japanese have started up again leads one to believe that, although they may never make a lot of money, their national pride may prove to be less expensive than that of either France or Britain.

It is perhaps wrong to give the impression that Japan is really starting again from square one. The break in aircraft engineering activity proved to be only five years in duration because of the Korean war. MacArthur, who was, according to his West Point Sergeant Major, a 'genuine genius' was also an unsentimental realist and he saw that the Korean War bill was going to be very high if aircraft were shipped to United States territory for repair. He therefore allowed Japanese companies to obtain repair and overhaul work on US military aircraft and the industry was allowed to officially re-emerge in April 1952. With such a short gap, present-day aircraft engineers can claim continuity with the aeronautical tradition which produced the aircraft for the Pacific War. They like to say that they do not start from scratch, they 'come back from Zero'.

In fact the early history shows some similarity with the industries of Western nations. Japan's first pilot qualified in France was licence No. 289 and a year later, in 1911, the first made in Japan aircraft took off with a certain Baron Narahara at the controls. This mixture of aristocrats and enthusiasts led to the creation of manufacturing companies whose identities have lasted to the present day. In 1918 Lt. C. Nakajima left the Imperial Japanese Navy and with a financial partner founded the Japanese Aircraft Manufacturing Works Ltd; later the partnership broke up and the two halves became Fuji Heavy Industries and Shin Meiwa. In the renascent aircraft industry these have just produced a multipurpose light plane, the F 200, and a new four-engined flying boat. During the thirties some planes including the Dakota were made under licence. During the war contact with the Axis powers was maintained by submarine and in this way the Japanese kept abreast of German developments including the Messerschmidt 109 E. the Me 163 rocket powered aircraft and German work on jet engines. In fact the first Japanese jet, the Nakajima Kikka, took the air just before the war ended.

The birth of the industry has been entirely under American auspices and its early licensed products were largely paid for by the Americans. Mitsubishi produced the Sabre fighters under licence for the Self Defence Force and F 104s Neptune patrol aircraft and various helicopters were made in the late fifties and early sixties.

During 1966 and 1967 the first two home-designed aircraft came onto the market, and the next generation of aircraft began to go onto the drawing boards. 1966 saw the first wholly Japanese aircraft, the YS 11 and the MU2, visit both the United States and Britain – on a sales tour; a Japanese aviation magazine has seen fit to start an international edition in English, and the first Japanese supersonic aircraft project has been given the green light by the Self Defence Agency. There are great wrangles going on about whether to begin a military or a civil jet transport and the Ministry of International Trade and Industry is reported to be mounting a world-wide market survey to define which aircraft will have the best export potential. In the Japanese aircraft industry in 1967 there were about 20,000 employees at work with an investment of £40 million. Since production began aircraft worth about £3000 million have been manufactured. By British standards this is hardly an impressive size but it is a promising beginning.

Interest at the moment centres on the YS 11. This is the largest and most sophisticated aircraft ever designed and manufactured wholly in Japan, except, that is, for the engines. It is wryly said that Japan makes the aircraft and Rolls Royce makes the profit; indeed the YS 11 is sometimes described as a twin-engined Viscount. Just as the original Viscount exploited the smooth and economical power of the early 1,000 h.p. Dart turbo-props so this aircraft is nicely matched to the later 3,000 h.p. Darts.

Two of these engines now develop more power than four of the early Darts and enable the YS 11 to carry up to sixty passengers with enough power in hand to give short field take-off.

The aircraft is a rather ugly shape, defying the dictum that an aircraft which looks right is right. The wings slant upwards in a pronounced dihedral whilst the tail is virtually flat and perched so far aft on the fuselage that it looks like an afterthought. The rudder is high and large and looks capable of counteracting any swing which could occur from an engine failure. The engines themselves are set fairly wide apart. Because of the demand for short take-off, extra large propellers were fitted to give maximum initial thrust; their large diameter of over fourteen feet, brought the tips of the propellers uncomfortably close to the fuselage and to the ground. Moving the engines further out on the wings eased the situation and also reduced the vibration felt in the passenger cabin. At the roots of the wings the fuselage is built out in a curious bulge because, on the early prototypes, the whole wing area between the engine and fuselage contributed virtually nothing to the lift. Indeed the YS 11 took a long time in the making and one story has it that the early wind tunnel tests were performed without the propellers rotating. When the full effects of this elementary mistake became apparent considerable modifications had to be undertaken. One of them was the fuselage bulge at the wing roots.

The YS 11 needed all the lift it could get because, like most of its competitors, it is aimed at the Dakota replacement market. Its objectives were to carry at least sixty passengers, to be able to use runways less than four thousand feet long, and to be profitable on short hops whilst keeping as high a cruising speed as possible. A turbo-prop rather than a turbo-jet engine was selected because it gives high initial thrust and acceleration and, because its economical cruising altitude is lower, short-range economy is possible. Top cruising speed has been sacrificed to give good take-off and landing performance, but even so the YS 11 is faster than its competitors like the Dart Herald and the Avro 748 with almost 300 m.p.h. at 15,000 feet.

Short field performance in large passenger aircraft is often regarded as being unnecessary. That concrete is cheaper than aircraft is a nostrum which the makers of the VC 10 have learnt with regret. Generally it is cheaper and easier to extend runways than to sacrifice operating economy. But this rule appears to be less applicable in the case of domestic airlines in developing countries. In the Philippines, for example, there are remote airfields left from wartime where getting cement, aggregate and reinforcement is a difficulty forever deferred until *manana*. It is administratively easier to buy an aircraft which can use existing airfields, if the sales pressure is fierce. Japanese salesmanship is hardly fierce but it is enthusiastic.

The more one looks at the YS 11 the more it becomes apparent that it was a very sensible choice of design for the first home-based attempt. The use of the Rolls Royce Dart engine removes much of the feeling that the aircraft is wholly new and unknown. Furthermore the continued development of the engine means that the aircraft may be stretched to compete even more effectively with earlier airframe designs. In building it, the Japanese have learned to cope with making large pressurised cabins if only for medium altitudes. They have been able to chance an innovation or two, as with their efficient retractable air stair. They have also been able to design fast turn-around features for ground handling.

An improved version is now on the market, the YS 11A in various configurations, either a 60-seater all passenger version, or a 46-seater mixed traffic one with 360 cubic feet of freight or an all-freight aircraft. The selling price is $1.3 million.

Early sales were disappointing. Filipinas Orient Airlines took three, but two were in lieu of reparations and one was leased. Most of the first thirty went to the Defence Agency or internal airlines like Japan Domestic, All Nippon and TOA. Nevertheless export sales were part of the original plan and the Japanese pressed on firmly. The target was a United States domestic airline and if such a sale could be made it really would be, to use a nineteenth-century metaphor, sending coals to Newcastle. To this end, the Japanese mounted a sales tour in the United States.

The historic flight began on 14 September 1966, when a YS 11 carrying ten extra fuel tanks in the fuselage made an overloaded take-off from Tokyo and headed for Wake Island. One hop of its trans-Pacific flight, the last 2,300 miles from Hawaii to San Francisco, was about double the YS 11's normal range. It was the first all-Japanese aircraft to land in the United States since the war and the event was a milestone in the renaissance of the Japanese aircraft industry. The tour was timed to coincide with the general meeting of the ALTA (Association of Local Transport Airlines) and thirteen airlines showed interest. Although during the subsequent sales tour there were places where nobody showed up, Atsushi Miyamoto, a director of the Nihon Aeroplane Manufacturing Company, came back early with the news that there were forty-three firm enquiries from six airlines. The current rate of production (one and a half aircraft a month) would need to be doubled to meet such an order, he added.

It's difficult to know if the Japanese understood that 'firm enquiries' were merely politeness, but they were undeterred. They tramped round South America and disposed of four aircraft in Peru and twelve in Brazil. Then Piedmont in the USA agreed to take ten with an option on ten more. Victory? Indeed so it seems, for although some of the early sales involved part-exchange deals for old aircraft and short leases which can have produced virtually nothing in the way of commercial returns, NAMC can now point to increasing operating experience, customer satisfaction, and contracts for money – in Piedmont's case $22.5 million. Further export orders have been obtained in Canada, the US and South America. Another opportunity is likely to be in Indonesia where Japan Air Lines are helping Garuda to reorganise the domestic network.

The production rate of YS 11s was stepped up to three a month and then five per month in 1968. Manufacture is divided among six private companies which are co-ordinated by NAMC. These companies include Mitsubishi, Kawasaki Aircraft, Fuji and Shin Meiwa. The plants where these aircraft are built are wartime assembly plants preserved in good condition but much of the design work was done in a university department. The design began in 1959 under the leadership of Professor Kimura at Tokyo University, with a team of between 50 and 100 designers, either from his own department or from industry.

Although the YS 11 gets most of the current limelight it is not the only aircraft with potential. The MU 2 is made by Mitsubishi without the benefit of government support like that extended to the YS 11. Mitsubishi did a lot of market research before they started to design their seven-seater business plane. They, too, decided that short take-off was an essential feature but they also decided to leapfrog one phase which could be discerned in the evolution of the same aircraft overseas. They decided to install turbo-prop engines instead of piston engines. There was no nonsense about designing for the home market. The United States was the target from the beginning. '42 per cent of America's 3,000 airports,' says Mitsubishi's handout, 'have runways no longer than 900 meters, it was proved essential . . . to permit taking off and landing even on a poorly paved short strip unusable for jet planes.' Mitsubishi put in American AiResearch engines as a further encouragement to the business customers and shipped them off to Mooney for distribution. The MU 2 has a pressurised cabin, cruises at 350 m.p.h. at 9,000 feet and has a range of 1,250 miles at 19,000 feet. It takes off in 500 yards and maintains seven passengers in pressurised comfort.

By mid-1968 over 30 MU 2's had been exported to the US, Switzerland and Sweden.

Whatever the future for these two particular aircraft one thing is clear, the Japanese can stand up in the world markets and make efforts at selling as credible as those made by the British, the Dutch and the French.

What about the future beyond the MU 2 and the YS 11? Professor Kimura ponders on the philosophy of the jumbo jet and appears to be considering a mini-jumbo jet transport with a fuselage so fat that there could be two aisles and no more three abreast seating. With this passenger appeal and advanced technology engines, such an aircraft could have an attractive future.

MITI's report suggests that the market ought to take to something like a 100-seater airbus capable of only 490 m.p.h. over as little as 600 miles range but showing low direct operating costs and short take-off capability. In 1968 the Japanese began to discuss joint development suggestions for this aircraft, the YX, from both Britain (BAC) and America (General Dynamics). Another aircraft going onto the drawing boards is a supersonic trainer which is to be built by Mitsubishi. A large anti-submarine flying boat has been built and it is reported to be especially good at landing in rough seas. The builders of the YS 11 have a design contract for a new CX or military transport which will have American engines whilst yet another MITI team is touring the world to define a successor to the Starfighter F 104.

Lest this burgeoning of aircraft projects should lead Western aero engine manufacturers like Rolls Royce and Pratt and Whitney to rub their hands in anticipation of further profits, MITI's Agency of Industrial Science and Technology has decided to develop a medium-sized jet engine of its own. This will have a thrust of between 20 and 30,000 lbs. and will be required for 'new types of aircraft to succeed Japan's YS 11'. If this development goes well, and it must be admitted that this is one of the tallest orders the Japanese could tackle, Japan will enter the seventies with a sophisticated aircraft industry of equal ranking with any in the world outside Russia and America.

But who pays? The YS 11 cost £5 million in government launching costs and NAMC had spent all its initial Government funds of £3 million by 1966. Proposals to puff this up to £8 million with a yearly subsidy of just under £1 million were barely adequate when the YS 11 was being produced at less than two every month. How much will be needed for all the new projects is anybody's guess, but the sums are sure to frighten some people. Engine developments must also cost many millions more.

Is it worth it when Japan is avowedly moving towards free trade and capital liberalisation? Japan will soon have to face American, British, French and Dutch competition without a protected home market and in this case the aircraft industry will have to move very fast to survive at all. Japan is, of course, surrounded by expanding markets in S.E. Asia, Taiwan and Korea, and even Red China may open up too. It is possible that these countries will give Japan a favoured position on ethnic grounds but the converse is just as arguable after what happened in the Pacific War.

On the other hand who but a naive optimist would have given Japan a hope in world shipbuilding back in 1950? Faced with Britain, Germany and the United States, where Liberty ships had poured from the yards, Japan's task must have seemed insuperable.

Getting the aircraft industry to follow the same amazing path sounds a very tall order indeed, but it has the confidence of youth, the backing of the Government – and access to a very able labour force. It has not got a great deal of money but with the economy back to a 9 per cent growth rate even that may be less of a restraint in the future.

FIVE

The Most Competent Bureaucracy

Government intervention in economic affairs is still a hotly debated subject in the West. Most of the discussion centres on the civil servants themselves rather than on the theoretical basis for intervention, and pragmatists point out that civil servants have not been conspicuously successful entrepreneurs. In general they are chosen to be analytical, impartial and unspecialised. In order to minimise the likelihood of corruption they are kept apart from industry, and close contact has been looked upon with suspicion.

From the beginning however Japan has had to face different problems because only the Government itself has been in a position to create industries which the country needed. The civil service has not therefore gone through a British phrase associated with gentlemanly supervision of *infra dig* activities like trade. Instead it has been concerned with keenly watching developments abroad and seeking to get them initiated in Japan. New industries, once created, have been sold off to private enterprise and the civil servants concerned have moved on to new initiatives. This is one of the reasons why Japan appears to have a most intelligent bureaucracy which, if economic success is anything to go by, must be one of the most effective in the world. It is interesting to see in detail what happens and the most interesting Ministry for visiting businessmen and for exporters and importers is MITI, the Ministry for International Trade and Industry.

MITI is a body which has no exact equivalent in other

nations, neither in its wide scope nor in its formidable reputation. Its members have wide powers of intervention at all levels in industry and trade and they are used with confidence and skill. It includes within its area of responsibility the Japan External Trade Organisation (JETRO) which among other things provides a world-wide intelligence service on how other nations run their economies. MITI takes upon itself tasks which most other countries would properly regard as the responsibility of the industries concerned. Recently, when the future of Japan's nascent aircraft industry was being debated, MITI planned to undertake a world-wide market survey of opportunities. No American company would dream of letting civil servants do such a job, and in Britain no one in the aircraft industry would believe a word of the survey even if it did come out on time. But in Japan this venture was completely unremarkable. This surprising competence is not just a feature of MITI alone, although it is this Ministry which gets the publicity because of its direct contact with industrial activity. Some other branches of the Japanese civil service operate in more familiar moulds. The responsibilities of the Ministries of Finance, Education, Agriculture and Forestry, Transport and so on are what one would expect. However, the civil servants themselves are distinct from most other nation's civil servants in that they are all qualified to some extent in mathematics. The Japanese like mathematics and are very fond of reeling off statistical information in order to prove a point. Nearly all Japanese high school students have to reach a proficiency in mathematics and physics that only the top American students attain, and to get into one of the four top Japanese universities, Hitotsubashi, liberal arts entrants have to have integral calculus and mathematics of a fairly high order.

The reputation of the civil service is so high that it is able to cream off the best the universities produce. Some of the most brilliant young men in Japan are to be found, for instance, in the Economic Planning Agency, a branch of the Prime Minister's Office. Here, as in MITI and elsewhere, they are determined to keep a quantitative grip on what is happening to Japan's economy. In fact Japan's economic policy is based on a more scientific and a more numerate analysis of desirable industrial trends than is the economic policy of any other country. This is only made possible by the widespread awareness of the need for quantifying both what is happening in Japan and what is happening elsewhere in the world.

One underlying reason for this most intelligent bureaucracy is that its members see their activities as contributing, not just to running a country, but to taking part in the great experiment of trying, by deliberate policy, to raise the living standards of the people. They are not idealistic automata, however, and there are more prosaic, though more surprising reasons why 'administrative guidance' from the civil service works so well in Japan.

For university graduates to get into the civil service in Japan is to start on the golden road to the top, not only in the civil service but at a later age in industry and politics as well. When it enters the civil service the graduate class of, say 1939, begins to move up step by step according to age. When the men of this intake are in their forties one of their age group in each Ministry will be given the top post (Vice Minister) in that department, a post equivalent to the British permanent secretary. The others from the class of 1939 will, by custom, resign. They will, however, also by custom, be found top jobs outside. The Vice Minister himself will only hold the post for a few years until he retires at fifty and follows his contemporaries to a top job outside.

From the Foreign Office, the fifty-year-olds go out to be Ambassadors, and from the Ministry of Justice they go out to senior legal posts. But from MITI and other economic departments like Finance, civil servants who got brilliant degrees twenty five years ago will be streaming out to join the boards of directors of big companies, banks, and business houses. Today's top men in many big companies, even in the huge Zaibatsu groups, were civil servants ten years ago. And the big companies like the system. It gives them top recruits of guaranteed intellectual quality in their late forties or early fifties for their boards of directors, and also close contact with the planning system which will henceforth be run by men whom their own directors knew as the most brilliant juniors immediately below them. The result is a cross-fertilisation of opinions, and a situation where some senior industrialists think of the bureaucrats as 'those bright young men who are doing all the hard research work'. That sort of attitude to government bureaucrats is very rare in other industrialised countries and it would be very difficult, for example, to find anyone in the Confederation of British Industries to speak in that tone of anyone in Whitehall.

Just as significant is the fact that similar cross-fertilisation occurs between the civil service and the political parties. The Cabinet Minister in charge of the Economic Planning Agency in 1967, Mr Miyazawa, was himself an ex-civil servant from former Prime Minister Ikeda's private office; he was pulled out of the civil service into politics before the rest of his class because Mr Ikeda wanted him in the cabinet. Mr Ikeda was the Prime Minister associated with Japan's original income—doubling plan. Mr Sato, the present Prime Minister, who previously ran MITI, is a former civil servant who entered politics in the more usual way. Prospects for a young man entering the Japanese civil service are very different from those in most other developed countries, except possibly France and Italy. In some of the Ministries, especially in MITI, the work itself is as exciting as in industry, and the other civil servants have not been preselected for their willingness to lead a life of grey anonymity.

Before looking at the economic planning apparatus, which cannot itself deploy any directly coercive weapons, it is as well to look in some detail at the executive ministry MITI. This controversial ministry does have some powers of direct intervention in the affairs of industry and it is the main channel through which 'administrative guidance' is exercised. Furthermore, it is the major channel of communication by which the wishes of industry become known to the Government.

One of its most interesting features is that it combines responsibility for technology with responsibility for international trade and for some domestic trading situations as well. In many other countries these functions are separated. In Britain, for example, the Board of Trade and the Ministry of Technology are quite separate, with a system of economic development councils reporting to a third body, the Department of Economic Affairs. In Japan all these eggs have been firmly in one basket since about 1950.

MITI runs a wide range of technology development laboratories, which include laboratories for textiles, mechanical engineering, fermentation, the chemical industry, and an institute for Industrial Arts. The headquarters of the Ministry contains a design centre where the importance of this commonly neglected aspect of manufacturing has long been emphasised. MITI has also been instrumental in setting up various inspection institutes for exported manufactures and in this way it has transformed the international reputation of Japanese goods. The standards imposed by the camera inspection institute, for example, have given Japanese cameras a reputation for high quality.

In certain other fields MITI has taken the technical initiative itself. One of its laboratories is currently building a giant computer to compete with the American Control Data Corporation's 6600 and the IBM 360–90s. The somewhat hesitant re-establishment of Japan's aircraft industry was also due to the initiative of MITI. Under MITI's wing come Power, Atomic Energy, Mining and the Patent Office. MITI also has responsibility for rationalising industries and is a notable provider of soft loans where these will promote desirable mergers.

Since the low productivity of small firms in Japan is an increasing drag on the economy, MITI has also spawned a separate Agency for their improvement and runs consultancy services for them. Thus, it has an important role in making inter-firm comparisons and using the information to sort out the strong from the weak.

In spite of its wide span of responsibilities MITI has a staff of only 12,000. This number of civil servants attends to a gross national product similar in size to that of Britain or Germany. In these countries government intervention in the affairs of industry is far less extensive than in Japan but the equivalent civil service departments are at least twice as large, and in the case of Britain, probably four times as large.

Any country intending to intervene in the affairs of industry on any scale would do well to study the example of MITI. Of course, Japan presents certain special features which arise from intense group loyalties and other social peculiarities. One that should not be omitted is the sheer pressure of entrepreneurship, which means that MITI is rarely called on to stimulate, but nearly always to guide and control an impetuous urge to expand. Nevertheless MITI itself is an expansionist force and argues the case for expansion to the Economic Planning Agency and the Ministry of Finance.

The Economic Planning Agency belongs to the office of the Prime Minister and, as in Britain and Germany, is separate from the executive departments of government. Its members doubt the extent to which they can really influence events. One of the Minister's former aides who now runs an economic research institute puts the matter even more succinctly: 'I agree that our Economic Surveys are rather good documents, but I'm not sure how many people actually read them. In judging them one must remember that the Japanese are very fond of mathematics, perhaps to an excessive extent.' Another observer, to whom this remark was retailed, admitted that this might be true but excused the defect by pointing out that those in charge of British economic policy must also have something of which they were excessively fond. 'Moralising perhaps?' 'Ah, yes, I can see that would be much worse'.

The real answer lies with the fact that administrative guidance is in the hands of very able civil servants in the executive ministries like MITI. There is a very close relationship between the EPA and MITI and indeed, the permanent secretary of EPA is himself ex-MITI. The EPA has educated MITI to behave in a more expansionist way than would come naturally to civil servants elsewhere, and this is true also of other executive departments.

There are great differences between western so-called planning and the Japanese EPA planning. The Japanese government publishes and keeps amending a running estimate of what, at present, it expects to be the movement in the country's main economic indicators during the twelve months ahead (for example in February, for the year following April 1967: 8 per cent rise in real GNP, 11.2 per cent in exports, 14.1 per cent in imports etc.). It keeps tabs on what is happening to the structure of the economy by a census of manufacturing every year, and of commerce every other year; more important it is ready to undertake sample surveys of almost any problem, not necessarily in depth but with sufficient quality to serve as a guide for indicative planning.

In what might be called the more static part of governmental analysis and planning the Japanese are mainly concerned to find out what is the trend of the productivity of capital and labour both in the economy as a whole and within particular industries; when there are clear signs that this productivity is declining in some fields, it becomes deliberate government policy to encourage new resources to move into newer fields instead. True, some protective cushions will be left or put in place to enable the resources still in these industries to stay there and improve their productivity. But the determination to get newer resources into more profitable lines for the future is specific and immense.

Even before these trends begin to show, however, what might be called the dynamic part of Japan's planning is based on a very careful analysis of production trends abroad. The object is to see what are the production patterns in countries richer than Japan. Then, since it is a datum assumption that Japan is going to get richer fast, the planners can tell from that what Japan's likely growth industries and likely declining industries will be. Moreover, marvellously strange calculations of entities like Japan's 'structural change coefficient' are made and published, in constant survey of whether Japan's economic structure is in fact changing in this right direction.

The principal mechanism by which Mr George Brown drew

up Britain's national plan in 1965 was that he wrote to various industries, and asked what they thought their level of production would be five years ahead. This methodology filled many Japanese with polite bewilderment. Why does Government want to know what industry thinks it is going to produce when what industry thinks is obvious in the production plans it already has in train? The object of planning is to find out whether trends in the structural change coefficient in other countries, trends in the marginal productivity of capital and labour, trends in such fortunately available live models of industrial production patterns of the future as the United States, suggest that what is thought by industry is likely to be wrong, because what industry will really have to be meeting, even by the end of this current year, is the market of tomorrow.

Some Japanese will say that when Government has formed its view, based on a full analysis of detailed statistics, and this view clashes with that formed by industry's or the trading houses' own market research surveys, then there can be argument about how hard the government should strive to ram its ideas down industry's throat. But Government must at least form its view, and publish it, before it can legitimately propagandise it. Otherwise, you do not have a mixed system, but only a completely non-forward looking one. The gap in concepts is as wide as that.

The point about Japanese planning and the interventionist bureaucrats is that they have attended to the most spectacular rise in economic power and living standards the world has ever seen. And this feat has been accomplished in the face of apparently insurmountable handicaps with only a negligible defence budget and some luck in the terms of international trade on the credit side of the balance. On *a priori* grounds it is reasonable to ask – does planning matter? There is still a reasonable academic case to be made out for restricting the role of Government as far as possible and leaving Adam Smith's market forces to do the rest. But in Japan there can be no doubt that large scale government intervention and indicative planning has worked.

The great flood of sophisticated concepts and statistical tables has been designed to inculcate a wholly different attitude towards modernisation and industrial progress than is prevalent in Britain. The climate in which industrial decisions are made is different from that in Britain and it seems quite probable that the decisions themselves reflect this. Somehow the civil service is better at being believed, not just because it is a better civil service, which it is, but mainly because it has addressed itself to the betterment of Japan and has gone about the job scientifically.

There is much to be said for sending to Tokyo a working party of economists if they would stoop to it, and some of the younger permanent secretaries and Treasury men, to report on whether there would be any advantage in changing the way Whitehall uses its own slide-rules. In fact there is much to be said for dissecting and setting out the whole story of Government, and industry interaction in Japan, not just for the benefit of faltering but advanced giants like the United Kingdom, but for countries like India, Mexico and Spain which are just running up to economic take-off.

SIX

Banks: Orthodox and Conventional

In writing about the Japanese banking system it has become almost a tradition to cite the words of a certain Mr Joseph M. Dodge of Detroit, an American banker who tried to impose a severe classic deflation on Japan towards the end of the Mac-Arthur era. He imparted some paternal advice to Japan on leaving its shores and his words have gone down in economic history mainly because everything he said was ignored. His advice was a terse distillation of conventional banking wisdom in an eminently quotable form. He said that Japanese financial circles were in the grip of dangerous delusions. Some of these were 'that increased production without a parallel increase in exports represents sound progress . . . that inflation can easily be offset by increased production. That a nation that must export to live cannot afford to price itself out of its export markets with a domestic inflation . . . that granting progressively larger amounts of commercial bank credit for capital purposes can be substituted for the normal processes of capital accumulation.' Mr Dodge viewed the favourable status of Japan in 1952 as the result of very fortunate external circumstances which were unlikely to recur. Mr Dodge returned to the United States, the deluded Japanese bankers took over the helm, rang full ahead all engines, and proceeded to steer Japan to the highest rate of sustained economic growth ever witnessed in the world.

Because Japanese companies live largely on bank loans, the power of the banks in Japan is much greater than in most other countries. Commonly only thirty per cent of their capital comes from shares, that is straight cash from the public. Therefore a Japanese company director has a subtly different relationship with his banker than his British or American counterpart.

Most Japanese commercial banks are heavily dependent on the central bank for their own credit base, so the central bank has great powers of control over the whole economy. When the Bank of Japan wants to make its wishes felt it can do so with a vengeance. Provided the central bank knows what it is doing this system has much to be said for it. Another advantage springs from the fact that the old orthodox capitalist assumption, that scattered shareholders working through the Stock Exchange are the best judges of where new money should be invested, is increasingly dubious when industrial and financial decisions have become so complex. Of course, large institutional investors such as insurance companies have increasing amounts of power in Western Europe by virtue of holding large blocks of shares, but this power tends to be unexercised except when take-over bids occur. Then, of course, one large corporate shareholder can make or break a company, but only at times of crisis. In Japan, however, a commercial bank, with its eagle eye nearer the account books and with its day-to-day involvement in industry, seems much more likely to show the right mixture of expertise, prudence and purposiveness.

Many of the banks were part of the pre-war Zaibatsu groups so they had a fair amount of expertise to call on. As Japanese development went on the firms associated with one particular bank would set up a new factory to exploit a new industry, for example, plastics. Immediately, the group around another bank would do the same and vigorous competition would commence. In a more orthodox economy those who leapt on the band wagon late would find that raising money on the market would be almost impossible, in which case the pioneer's lead would be unchallenged. Not so in Japan, however, where it seems likely that the economy has benefited considerably from what those on the band wagon always call 'excessive' competition.

This kind of picture however is more true of the fifties and early sixties than of today.

One point is that the banks in themselves seem to have slightly less power than they had five years ago. Part of the reason is that industries are larger and better established so they feel their own strength rather more. One banker, when asked to comment on the competition engendered by different rival banks, had this to say: 'Five years ago the main decision on whether to set up a new industry within our group would probably have been taken in this office. But now, any new industry is likely to be in some sense an offshoot of an existing industry. So if it was some new sort of chemical that was in question, then it would be the President of the chemical company in our group whose ideas would probably be most decisive; if it was some engineering product, then the President of our heavy industries group. Mind you, the views of the bank President are still very important; but so are the views of the trading company associated with our group, and of the real estate company . . . .'

Within groups that are less tightly knit, one notices the same trend. Five years ago, it was quite common to find industrialists who positively preferred to do as much of their borrowing as possible from a single bank. 'Then, if hard times come, we are very important to that bank, and they can hardly afford to let us go bust.' But now Japanese companies have grown so large that they have to draw their loan funds from two or more banks. 'The ideal is to borrow enough from each of one's main reference banks so as to be important to them – and usually particularly important to one – but not so much from that one bank that it is in all circumstances all-important to you. Things are more comfortable if you can have this delicate balance, although such comfort is admittedly not always attainable.'

A second impression, although many Japanese would deny this, is that governmental intervention in the economic system has actually grown in extent within the internal economy since 1962, and partly at the bankers' expense. A main reason is that Japan's drive into new industries has reached the stage (e.g. in petrochemicals and in automobiles) where it is simply not economic for Japan to have a separate firm sponsored by each of the seven or eight big banking groups or even by each of the *ad hoc* marriages between groups which come naturally to some of them. So the bureaucrats are now saying 'merge'. 'There are two chief difficulties in the way of such mergers,' said one Japanese involved in the process. 'First, under our lifetime employment system, the interests of the staffs concerned. Secondly, the fact that the proposal will usually have to be to merge a firm under the influence of one big bank with a firm under the influence of another big bank, and the banks concerned often do not like it.' Obviously, they are especially likely to express their dislike the more forcibly – though even then, by Western standards not quite to the bitter end – if the proposal is to merge firms across the frontiers of the empires of the three famous ex-Zaibatsu groups (Mitsubishi, Sumitomo, Mitsui). The other big banking groups (which might aptly be described as 'not quite ex-Zaibatsu, although they would like to be') perhaps tend to be more amenable.

While big firms are dependent on finance from the banks, small firms are dependent on a sea of I.O.U.'s. The extent to which the Japanese economy floats on a flood-tide of mutual trading credits is astonishing to a foreigner. In normal times, and on the surface, it may seem reasonably orthodox. A manufacturing concern will sell its produce to a trading house against three-months bills, the trading house passes it down through other wholesalers and sub-wholesalers for similar I.O.U.'s and only the final personal consumer pays cash.

But when the Bank of Japan has to tighten monetary policy, the effect on this great volume of intra-trade credit is cataclysmic. Everybody wishes to get money or credit, and the large firms are likely to be most successful in securing it. At such periods, a large manufacturer buying components from a small sub-contractor will insist on paying in longer and longer paper, stretching to nine or ten months 'pregnancy bills' in some instances; the smaller or shakier firm, whose creditors rightly fear is more liable to go bankrupt, will find it more difficult to get similar easy terms for buying its raw materials. Hence the so-called 'bankruptcy whirlwinds' among small firms at times of squeeze. It is a cruel system; but, if the aim of a squeeze is to hit hardest at the least efficient firms, it is probably the right one for the economy.

Curiously enough in spite of latent demand the discount market in bills is very poorly developed. A small industrialist needing quick money to pay wages for example, cannot ring up a broker in Tokyo and cash a bill for 20 per cent less than face value. If he sees a squeeze coming he can try to export because he will get cash from trading companies (who themselves may borrow the money wherever they are operating; New York, London etc.). This is one of the reasons why Japanese credit squeezes do provoke export booms. But, in general, he will find very little room to manoeuvre. The main reason is that the amount of actual cash that the city banks carry is very small. It may be as low as two or three per cent, ten times less than that regarded as conventional in Britain. The rest of the deposited money no sooner comes in than it goes out again at high interest rates. It may sometimes go out to another bank that needs cash but the 'call money' interest rates sometimes soar to fantastic heights like 20 per cent. Not surprisingly very few have found it really worthwhile to set up in the business of discounting bills inside Japan.

Not every enterprise in Japan draws money from the banks or lives on rotating I.O.U.'s. There is a quite separate sphere of business activity that operates strictly for cash and more or less finances itself. Occasionally it even finances the banks. One Western businessman put it like this: 'If some guardian angel said he would give me one of the big Japanese business groups for Christmas, I wouldn't choose Mitsui or Mitsubishi. I'd choose one of the groups that the outside world has never heard of, because they don't engage in international trade. There are some very fly gentlemen who own, for example, private commuter railway lines. They have made huge profits from real estate development on the sites they own. They have branched into department store empires, often placed at strategic points through which their commuters have to pass. They've gone into the entertainment business. Their aim is to get hard cash from the consumer, while those other groups like Mitsui, which the world has heard of, are just passing round bits of paper. These strictly internal, strictly-for-cash, groups are the only people in this country who are not dependent on the banks; on the contrary the banks come running to them.'

Certainly the giant department stores on city rail termini could well be copied in the West. They are a convenience to the public and help to swell the use of commuter trains in off-peak periods. In general, however, it would be fair to comment that the cash-only groups are engaged in fields where the Japanese public is not being well served. The story of property development in the big cities is a tragedy; housing conditions are the one sector in which Japan lags very badly indeed behind the affluent countries of the west. The commuter railways are famous for employing pushers to compress passengers into a density of travelling flesh that would shatter the Royal Society for the Prevention of Cruelty to Animals. Other notable omissions are chain stores and supermarkets. The entertainment industry, outside the wholly admirable national television service NHK, is following a familiar decline: cinemas are emptying and the Japanese film industry is getting down to crude sex and X-certificate violence to keep the customers coming in.

Quite what would have happened in these areas if they had been developed within the orbits of sober and respectable banks is hard to say. No country has the answer to commuter comfort, and the collapse of the film industry under the impact of television appears unavoidable. Japanese cities are certainly ill-planned, uncomfortable chaos but nice 'semi-detacheds' are not particularly productive investments and the social ills arising from what might be regarded as slum living are not yet apparent in Japan.

Except for certain comparatively small areas then, the influence of Japanese banks permeates the whole economy and provides a means by which the central bank can influence economic activity in a very subtle manner. This will be seen to be of vital importance when the techniques employed during a recession come to be considered in a later chapter.

So far this chapter has considered Japanese banks as lenders to industry and it may have given an impression of business with tycoons who feverishly spend on ever more efficient plant to earn profits to pay back ever-mounting interest. Although this is not wholly unfair, it must be remembered that the Japanese people are among the world's keenest savers. As individuals, they pay cash and get very little on credit except petrol. Hire purchase is rare. One of the world's most vigorous consumer durable industries has so far sold its television sets, tape recorders, washing machines, motor bicycles and air conditioners for cash and only recently has consumer credit begun to attract the banks.

An international comparison of consumer credit shows that outstanding balances are lower in Japan (on a *per capita* basis) by a ratio of about thirty to one compared to the United States, and six to one compared to Britain. Expressed as a percentage of gross national product Japan (at 1.5 per cent in 1964) is still well below West Germany, Britain and the United States. Top of this particular poll, by the way, is Canada at over 12 per cent.

One reason for this is the practice of paying up to 40 per cent of wages as a twice-a-year bonus. The average worker therefore gets windfall sums of up to £200 a time. Either he banks them to save for his children's education or his own old age, or he buys an expensive consumer durable. The coming of the motor car, however, is disturbing this pattern because the unit cost is bigger than the usual bonus.

So far the consumer credit that exists has been provided mainly by the shops and distributors. Invariably these deals were refinanced by the banks in a credit squeeze. Instead of blanket cuts in hire purchase activities as tends to happen in Britain, the Japanese first squeeze the least credit-worthy distributors and shops. The strong survive and the weak get a nasty lesson. Nevertheless direct consumer credit is now being developed. The reasons the banks originally turned their attention to the consumer lay in the general shortage of funds in the early sixties boom. The banks were frightened by a shift from indirect to direct investment (i.e. more shares and stocks) so in order to attract deposit money they widened the range of services on offer and dangled the carrot of consumer credit to back up the attractions of security. These measures made little impact until the boom of 1963 but thereafter, even through the recession of 1964 when new credit restraints were imposed, the trend to 'mass banking' continued.

Banks now offer a variety of personal loans, and some of these are earmarked for specific purposes such as the acquisition of consumer durables. Terms of maturity are up to 24 months so here the banks are functioning almost in the way of hire purchase companies. Interest is only around 10 per cent. There is still no development of the idea of 'credit worthiness' on a personal basis.

The most famous of the Japanese banks are, of course, those which were once the centres of the pre-war Zaibatsu, Sumitomo, Mitsubishi and Mitsui. Top of the heap at present, however, is Fuji with over £1,600 million deposited. The old Zaibatsu used to have regular meetings of top industrial bosses where decisions as important as those of the Government itself were taken, and there are still traces of this tradition in, for example, the meetings of the Fuji group. This 'is a getting-together of firms with close business connections with the Fuji bank; they discuss such business developments as are to their mutual benefit', or so says the Fuji chairman, Mr Iwasa. It does now seem true that the character of these banks is fundamentally different from what it was pre-war. Fuji has not only gone out to be a people's bank, leading in the consumer credit movement, but many of its major industrial borrowers have heavy obligations to other rival banks.

Furthermore any manipulation that does go on seems to be undertaken by the Bank of Japan, as the instrument of the Japanese Government. The commercial banks themselves form a kind of circulatory system with connections to nearly every party of the body of industrial Japan. Like the human circulatory system their function is not just nourishment, but communication and control as well.

SEVEN

High Investment and the Unacquisitive Society

A detailed consideration of what makes Japan tick, is one sure way of demolishing a good number of the axioms of conventional Western economic wisdom. Nonetheless there is one feature of Japan which triumphantly vindicates one bit of conventional wisdom and that is the economic principle that high investment leads to economic growth. Whilst almost every other feature of the Japanese scene can be accounted for in ways which are mutually contradictory, the fact of their high investment and its relation to economic growth is obvious and unarguable, and the really interesting question is how the Japanese arrange for this investment to be as high as it is.

First, a table to point the moral:

Average Investment and Growth Rates, 1956-63

	% of GNP going to capital formation	Average annual % growth of GNP
Japan	34	10.1
West Germany	25	6.3
Italy	23	6.0
France	21	4.9
Canada	24	3.8
Sweden	22	3.7
Belgium	19	3.0
USA	17	2.8
Britain	17	2.6

This high rate of capital investment has been kept up, even though the marginal productivity of newly introduced capital equipment to those who instal it has fallen off in recent years. Investing a million yen now will earn less money than it would have a few years back. It is important to realise therefore that a large part of the investment programme is not free-market-induced in the western sense, rather it is more deliberately arranged.

This 'blind rush for industrial gadgetry' is increasingly attacked by such visiting species as American business efficiency experts who can be heard to talk like this: 'These people must be riding for a fall. Their businessmen are piling in new investment without any regard for its profitability, without any proper cost accounting, it's just for the glory of the new Japan.' And it must be admitted that, at a casual glance, the steel industry investment programme, for example, has looked as disaster prone as any novice setting off on a sixth grade climb in the Dolomites. The motive is often, 'Well, if other nations can do it, so can we.' Currently the Japanese are aiming at a staggering 70 million tons of steel a year. The figure corresponds to the same *per capita* consumption as that of West Germany. The climb in steel capacity will be so steep that in five years or so the increase will equal the absolute total of British capacity.

But Japanese planners have a sophisticated way of making reassuring noises. This was how one of them described the general thinking behind the high investment: 'Down to about 1961, the marginal productivity of capital was rising in this country; we reckon that an average £100 investment in 1955 was able to give the pretty extraordinary yield of £50 per year in value added, and by 1961 the even more extraordinary yield of £68 a year. While this was going on, it was easy to keep the investment boom afire. In those days new capital equipment was either adding to total capital equipment, or else was replacing old and very inefficient equipment. The trouble now is that the capital equipment which new investment replaces is not so old. According to our censuses: in 1955 more than 43 per cent of the capital equipment that was being used in Japan's manufacturing industry was over six years old; but by 1964 only 27 per cent was. It is therefore natural that some of our manufacturers are less eager to invest, because the machinery they will be to some extent rendering superfluous is not the antiquated machinery they used to know and despise. But these people are looking at matters only in their static context. In the dynamic context, it is quite obvious that, with an ever speedier international rate of rising technological progress, equipment is going to become outdated and lose its real international competitiveness even more quickly than before. So, even when there is a surplus of not-so-antiquated equipment, the job of government is so to organise fiscal policy, so to organise lending policy so to organise administrative guidance, in order to use every short, medium and long term weapon to see that new investment has simply got to be kept up. Provided, of course, it is investment in the right places.'

This last provision is, of course, a crucial one but the Japanese bureaucrats think they have that under control as well. (See Chapter 5).

The point to note here is that an increasing part of Japan's high rate of investment is what can best be called 'forced draught investment' induced by government policies of deliberate expansion. So the next question which arises is how can the Japanese induce forced draught investment on the present scale, pushing the ratio of investment to national income to twice that of the United Kingdom and America yet still avoid running into massive internal inflation?

In crude terms the main reasons appear to be these. Firstly Japan devotes 17 per cent more of her national income to productive investment than Britain does because her defence expenditure is one sixth the size. It is just over 1 per cent as against 7 or 8 per cent. The second reason is that personal consumption in Japan takes nearly 10 per cent less of the national income than it does in Britain.

The question of defence expenditure is probably going to have increasing geopolitical significance. It is no coincidence that the two powers which were defeated in World War II have both shown high rates of growth. Although German defence expenditure has risen greatly in recent years, in both Germany and Japan the fact that their defence has been undertaken by other countries has been not only a saving for them but an additional handicap to their trade competitors. In the United States, at least until the Vietnam war, comparatively unproductive defence expenditure did not matter very much because the country was so very rich, but for the United Kingdom it has become a very important factor in the slow rate of economic growth. Furthermore the effect increases by compound interest every year and has become so obvious recently that the Government is being compelled to take notice. Trade liberalisation and free competition between nations will increasingly mean that defence burdens must become equal too, at least in terms of the respective proportions of gross national product. The disparity in defence expenditure between Britain and Japan only accounts for 6 or 7 per cent of the total difference of 17 per cent. The remaining 10 per cent seems to match the extra percentage of personal income that the average Japanese saves: the worker puts aside nearly 20 per cent of his personal income as opposed to only 8 per cent in America or Britain. Is that the whole story? Do the Japanese really qualify for the honour of being the most thrifty people in the world?

A closer look at the figures makes the situation rather less clear-cut. For one thing a good deal of the Japanese worker's saving is done for him because as we have noticed he gets up to 40 per cent of his wages in half-yearly bonuses paid in arrears. This money has to be spread out to cover the next six-monthly period so even the poorer families have to have savings accounts at the banks. Another factor is that fringe benefits frequently do some of the worker's spending for him. Paying for his transport costs to and from work and subsidising the company's cheap shops does not show up in the company's wage bill but it does mean that the worker's apparent wages are less than they really are, so money saved appears to be greater in proportion. Furthermore, providing company houses for workers shows up as capital investment on behalf of the company, whereas in the

West the cost of this housing would show up as personal spending on the part of the worker.

These considerations make a dent in that virtuous figure of 20 per cent. The moral approbation still due to the thrifty worker can be further reduced by remembering that he has to save money for his children's education. Yet another factor is the practice of paying retirement pensions as lump sums which have to be banked and again show up as personal deposits.

None of these qualifications really affect the magic figure of 34 per cent of the gross national product which goes into capital formation. Although one may quibble about exactly where the money comes from one has only to see Japan to realise that investment in social capital like houses is very low, whilst productive investment in manufacturing plant is very high.

The fiscal system is a major contributory factor in all this, and although it looks very orthodox by Western standards, it is actually very expansionary.

Thus one can read in the newspapers at budget time that the Japanese Cabinet has decided, after a long session, that the planned rate of growth of national income for the new fiscal year should be 9.0 per cent. This apparently absurd guessing game, often expressed to very precise decimal points, has a real economic importance. For every 0.1 per cent of the agreed target rate for growth in the national income, the Japanese reckon that they can expect a stated amount of extra tax revenue on the basis of existing tax rates. By the rules of the normal budget-balancing game, this – together with any sums carried over from previous years – is then assumed to be available for deliberate increases in government expenditure or for new tax reliefs (especially to business). In expansionary and inflationary years, which in Japan means in most years, the government thereby continues with what are really still expansionary budget policies. In deflationary years, when the expected growth in the national income does not look so large, such as 1966, the Japanese very sensibly abandon this system; they planned in that year for a deliberate budget deficit instead.

Of course, there is a considerable element of forced saving –

of the Keynesian or neo-Marxist technique of bringing down money apparently from the moon in what orthodox people would call inflationary financing, and pumping it into artificially high investment – in the Japanese economy. And, of course, there has to be in any economy which is pushed along by a fantastic investment rate of over 30 per cent of gross national product.

But what about the man who actually makes the investment, the businessman himself, what goes on inside his head?

It is not possible to understand the Japanese businessman if the model one has in one's mind is a classical capitalist entrepreneur. Such a man (who is admittedly difficult to find as a pure specimen even in the West) lives by maximising the short-term gains on the money entrusted to him, and if he makes a large profit he may pay out large dividends and thereby attract even more money from the waiting army of shrewd investors. This acquisitive man who knows that avarice is the springs of industry barely exists in Japan. Business in Japan operates on quite different assumptions and visiting foreign businessmen must expect a cultural shock. American cost accountants in particular tend to reel in alarm at their first glimpse of a Japanese balance sheet.

The average President of a large Japanese company is only rather minimally interested in the return on his shareholders' yen. The shareholder has provided only 20 or 30 per cent of the capital anyway, the other 70 or 80 per cent has come from the bank. Of course the shareholder deserves at least a customary dividend, probably about 10 per cent. If this can be pushed up, then these rather speculative counters called shares can have a boom which makes the President popular. But the Japanese industrialist's main obligations lie in quite different directions. His first responsibility is to his workers who expect a lifetime's employment out of him. Next come the executives, the older ones first and they expect to be protected from such discomforts as having bright young men promoted over their heads. The President also feels an intense loyalty to the firm or the group of firms he belongs to and wishes deeply to see it march on to new glories, perhaps by increasing its range of brilliant new products or by raising total production but not by maximising profitability. Beyond the firm, the next and last thing for which he feels intense group loyalty is Japan herself.

All this leads to the odd result that a recent Japanese economic survey could report in the same breath that 'the ratio of corporate income to total national income in Japan is the highest in the world', and yet that 'the gross capital profit rate (ratio of profit before tax to gross capital) is still lower than that of western countries . . . due to the fact that Japanese enterprises have poured in more investment in equipment and facilities than their western counterparts.' Western businessmen may say that this provides them with an opportunity to set up profitable enterprises in Japan which would not join the mad rush for investment at any price; would attract a skilled working force by paying higher wages out of that excessive total corporate income; and would, in particular, attract by higher salaries a lot of bright young executives who must be resentful of working under elder deadbeats in Japan's hierarchical firms.

If it were profitable in Japan to run businesses this way one may be sure that someone would already be doing it. The reasons that no firm of any size has yet climbed off the high investment bandwagon are not easy to discern. It may just be that the group loyalties are too strong. If the industrialist were immune from group loyalties by virtue of being a foreigner he would, for that reason, find a new difficulty, that of creaming off the bright young executives from his competitors. In good Japanese firms young executives are offered security and automatically higher wages as they grow older; this is something foreign firms don't give and it makes the future uncertain.

For an industrialist not to follow the investment rush therefore takes courage and there is always the sneaking suspicion that it could be unsound not to, especially in an economy that is changing so rapidly.

In recent years the most spectacular boom was in petrochemicals and it provided a classic example of infectious high investment. Taking their cue from petrochemical progress abroad the group around one bank set up a firm to build a plant. Then the group around a rival big bank did the same thing almost as a matter of face. The rush continued to such an extent that MITI had to step in with powers to veto any proposal the bureaucrats deemed unwise.

The same rush is currently happening in steel. In February 1967 the dynamic President of Yawata had just threatened to start work on a huge new investment programme 'if current negotiations for adjusting plant and equipment investments were unnecessarily protracted'. The equally dynamic President of Sumitomo Metal was stressing the 'need for further efforts for voluntary adjustment of such investment', but then his investment programme at Wakayama had been started two years before. Again the government is thinking of restraining things somehow, this time by encouraging mergers (e.g. Yawata – Fuji) so as to reduce the number of industrialists who play chicken with investments of millions.

The danger that an investment drive might go dangerously haywire when it is spurred more by fierce group loyalties than by close profits analysis has been mitigated partly by the influence of an unusually competent bureaucracy, and partly by the control retained over investment funds by the banks.

It can be convincingly argued that the Japanese have actually managed to overcome one of the weaknesses of the normal western free enterprise system – which is that the total of investment that seems profitable to individual profit-seeking firms is unfortunately almost invariably smaller than a dynamic economy should require.

Equally unfortunately it does not seem that the Japanese answer to the problem will survive being exported to other countries in need of economic growth and high investment.

EIGHT

Cameras: The Saturated Market

Japanese camera makers are in a position which is at once both embarrassing and funny to behold. They have cleaned up the world market and most of them simply don't know what to do next. Their own worried words convey some of the comic element in their situation. The Japan Light Machinery Information Centre says, 'In science, both pure and applied, in industry and in commerce . . . as indeed in life itself, the law, as rigid and inflexible as that of the Mede and Persian, is written for all: Advance or Fall Back. If you cannot, or will not go Forward, then, do what you will, you cannot stay where you are. Fall Back, you must.' They go on to invite you to see their cameras.

Whether the businessman's curious metaphysics are valid or not, the words do reflect the uneasiness of some of the world's most successful entrepreneurs who have gone about as far as they can go. In 1965 they had to organise an anti-depression 'cartel' to stop themselves from dumping their products and, in 1966, unusual for a Japanese industry, production fell 15.7 per cent – by agreement. Even so the Japanese industry churned out 3,145,000 cameras valued at $121.6 million. The big year had been 1964 when $4\frac{1}{2}$ million cameras were produced and West Germany's export record was beaten in terms of value. This is the interesting fact; it means that Japan exports the more expensive kind of camera and that it is the advanced sophisticated West European nation that is left churning out vast numbers of cheaper cameras, a complete reversal of what might have been expected.

Here are the figures. In 1966 Japan exported 1,894,000 units, value $66.8 million, Germany exported 2,238,000 units which were worth only somewhere between $30 and 40 million. Both countries export over 50 per cent of their total production. So the old image of Japan producing millions of simple cameras by using cheap labour is finally dispelled. And in the eyes of MITI the camera industry matters a lot, because it accounts for one per cent of all Japan's exports.

Before looking at what the camera makers are going to do next, it's worth looking back at two major contributions to their present embarrassing success. One, of course, was technological innovation but the other provides an interesting example of successful government intervention in the affairs of industry.

In the early fifties when Japan was beginning to export to world markets again, her goods still carried the pre-war stigma of being cheap and nasty copies of other people's products. Germany's optical products were the epitome of high-quality precision engineering. Names like Leica, Voigtlander and Rollei implied customer satisfaction extending back for decades. To compete with this the Japanese decided that since nobody would believe any advertising campaigns, the lenses and cameras would have to speak for themselves. Accordingly they established a Camera Inspection Institute to apply the provisions of laws concerning standards passed in 1948 and 1958. The Institute came into existence in 1954 when it was established by the Government as an autonomous non profit-making body. It is located in a modern building in the middle of Tokyo which is packed with advanced inspection equipment. The staff consists of something over a hundred devoted scientific watchdogs who, apart from being highly qualified in physics and electronics, have served a two-year apprenticeship in detecting substandard cameras and lenses.

The inspection is based on the random sampling of batches of two hundred or so cameras at a time. If more than a certain small percentage fail to meet the required quality minima, the entire batch goes straight back to the manufacturers. If there are fewer substandard cameras than the agreed proportion the batch is passed and only the defective ones are returned. The penalty of having, say two hundred cameras blacked because a few bad ones turn up is a heavy one, and as often in Japan, the loss of face and the bureaucrats' displeasure also constitute a serious setback. Over the years this procedure has given Japanese optical equipment a shining reputation for quality and reliability which has paid off handsomely.

There are two main Inspection Institutes, one for still and ciné cameras, and the other for telescopes. These Inspection Institutes are themselves subject to inspection by MITI's own Industrial Manufactures Inspection Institute, which itself also inspects microscopes, and acts as any other kind of inspector if a buyer's contract requires it.

It might be thought, at least by British observers, that such a formidable barrier would remove most of the impulse to export but this is far from being the case.

The other factor which really boosted the industry in the period from 1958 to 1960 and which has helped to ensure the obsolescence of successive generations of equipment is technological innovation.

To take really good pictures the photographer needs complete control of a large number of variables. The length of time the film is exposed is probably the most important, followed by the range of the object of interest and the depth of the field the photographer requires to have in focus. These two factors are controlled by the focus and the aperture or F stop which also influences the exposure. If a photographer wishes to take close-up pictures of say, the first spring snowdrop or a postage stamp, he also needs to know the parallax between the picture which actually falls on the film and the picture he sees through the viewfinder. Lastly a photographer needs to select a suitable lens at will, and one for taking a distant mountain scene will be different from one for close-up work.

To have complete control of all these variables, the early post-war photographer needed to carry many separate items. Apart from the camera, he needed a separate range-finder and exposure meter and if he wanted to take close-ups he had to mount the camera on a tripod, remove the film to find the actual view through the lens and then reload the film. There were, of course, many partial answers to these problems; the twin lens reflex camera was one, and built-in range finders on 35 mm. cameras were another. Of course the Box Brownie didn't need any of this elaboration but it didn't take the best pictures either. The opportunity for technical innovation was therefore very great and with each new step the previous best camera was made obsolete. In this way a consumer market became virtually fashion-conscious.

One major landmark in this technical evolution was the electric eye camera in which the exposure was set automatically by a built-in, light sensitive, photo-electric cell. One such camera was, as the makers rather uncharitably described it, literally foolproof. Using a Kodapak cartridge, all the photographer had to do was point it, select a distance scale, short, medium or long range, and press the button. The film speed rating, the F stop and the shutter speed were selected automatically and ordinary snapshot pictures appeared through an F 2.8 lens with a quality that could hardly be bettered by a professional. For those who required something less foolproof and more flexible the same electric eye technology produced cameras in which the film was wound on electrically but the shutter was semi-automatic or manual. The sales slogan is as esoteric as an electronic advert: one camera has 'an electronic shutter (diaphragm priority type) with CdS light-sensing cell and four high-performance transistors'.

At present fierce competition has led to stalemate among the manufacturers. Asahi, Canon, Minolta, Nikon and Yashica all make broadly similar products and in some markets they have agreed to freeze their relative shares. The Japanese home market is near saturation, the United States and European markets are growing only very slowly and only in South America is business booming. By far the most common camera is still the 35 mm with the shutter between the lenses and of these, the single lens reflex is the most advanced.

As an example of the extremes to which technical progress

has been taken one could look at the Olympus Pen F. This company pioneered the half-frame camera in which a 35 mm standard film is used twice as it were, to produce the so-called half-frame picture. This camera is therefore smaller and lighter than even the standard 35 mm camera, and with a focal plane shutter it is possible to change lenses as and when required. Shrewdly, it has been arranged that other manufacturers' lenses will fit. It is a single lens reflex camera in which the image falling on the film is intercepted and fed to the viewfinder. In this way all parallax, focus and depth of field problems are solved without the possibility of error. The exposure meter is mounted inside the camera and measures incident light after it has passed through the lens.

There are no doubt many more innovations possible but they are not so radical as to make existing cameras obsolete. Nikon have produced a camera that can be used under water but it would be optimistic to think that it will sell a million. Canon have produced a lens that gathers more light than the human eye. Some manufacturers detect a trend to bigger film sizes, and one recently marketed is the 220 mm. Polaroid is another unknown quantity. Will it become cheaper? In general, film limitations make it unlikely that cameras will get even smaller than the half frame size. In general, too, technical trends are hard to see. Assuming that there is no automatic transfer from still cameras to ciné (and the jump still seems too great for most people) it does appear that the days when a new technological trick could make all previous cameras obsolete have gone for good.

Companies therefore face stagnation and some may even have to contract. They are all looking for ways in which they can continue to grow but still employ the optical and precision engineering skills which they have developed so highly. One of the first companies to find a solution to these problems is the Olympus company which has a long history of inventiveness.

Olympus's future lies with a potentially very lucrative field, medical or bio-engineering. If it plays its cards right it may not even have to venture outside the field of optics. This company already devotes half its energies to activities which have nothing to do with cameras: Olympus makes microscopes very successfully and it makes measuring devices and medical instruments. Its long history of microscope-making has given it some of the clearest pointers to the potentialities of this market.

Olympus in fact made microscopes even before the war. During the war it moved away from a devastated Tokyo to Nagano Prefecture, a pleasant sub-alpine upland region of lakes and small farms where mulberry trees grow well. For this reason it has long been a centre of the silk industry and a labour force of nimble-fingered workers was readily available. Japan never had radar during the war and enormous effort went into optical sights and range-finders. After the war both the microscope and camera side of the business expanded rapidly and the company also began to make endoscopes for internal examinations of the stomach.

The early stomach or gastrocameras were relatively clumsy. They had to be swallowed under anaesthesia and it was difficult to tell what they were pointing at when inside the stomach. The basic principle was simple; it was merely a matter of swallowing a small camera on the end of a wire, air was then pumped into the stomach and the camera triggered, a small flash went off and the direction of the camera was noted by observing the flash through the stomach wall and by taking an X-ray picture at the same time. The film was wound on from an outside control box and the procedure repeated, after manoeuvring the camera to a new position. That was in 1950.

Now, Japan has one medical problem peculiar to herself and that is the highest proportion of stomach cancer in the world. Half of all cancer in Japan is stomach cancer and it is so common that a case for public health screening can be made out. The trouble, until recently, was that gastroscopy required a patient to enter hospital and any mass screening was out of the question on purely economic grounds.

Olympus set about developing a gastrocamera which could be used on a mass scale. They succeeded so well that one camera can be swallowed with no more than a local spray anaesthetic at the back of the throat. This can be operated by any general practitioner who can then send off the films for expert examination. If there is anything suspicious the patient is called back for further investigation using more complex cameras.

Fibre optics are responsible for some of the more surprising advances in this field. By connecting the swallowed camera to a fibre it is possible for the doctor to manoeuvre the camera until something of interest comes into view. He can then trigger the camera to photograph with flash from inside the stomach and can also photograph from the outside down the fibre optic. He can apply his eye to the viewfinder and manoeuvre a pair of biopsy forceps from inside the camera to take a sample of the stomach lining, alternatively he can flush the cells for cytological examination with a jet of water. Thirty-six exposures in full colour can then be examined at leisure.

Also coming on to the market soon will be an endoscope which can be inserted at the other end of the intestinal tract. These techniques enable explorations to be made which would have once required a full exploratory operation with general anaesthesia.

One huge and unexpected market for gastroscopes and cameras has turned out to be aviation. The cameras are used to inspect the guts of jet engines and other inaccessible parts of aircraft and, so great are the economic benefits of shortened inspection times, that this market is liable to expand faster than the medical market.

In medicine there are other opportunities for sophisticated optical devices like retinal cameras and microscopes for use during operations. Canon has also entered this field with specially developed bright lenses which intensify the light from X-ray fluoroscopes. By the use of mirrors they have produced a lens of F 0.56, almost certainly the world's brightest, thirteen times brighter than the human eye. With its use the company claim great advances in X-ray inspection techniques and a considerable diminution in the extent to which patient and doctor are exposed to radiation. Canon is also venturing outside the optical industry and has gone into the desk computer field. So has another manufacturer, Ricoh, with desk copying machines for good measure. The others are still thinking but in general the camera industry's future is in soft focus. 'Advance they must?' It remains to be seen.

NINE

Steel: The Backbone of the Country

The iron and steel industry was justifiably described by pre-war economists as a commanding height of the economy in an industrial country. The metaphor reflected the language of the class war and it was believed that control of the steel industry would be essential to a successful proletarian revolution. The industry was regarded as a sort of header tank from which a cheap primary industrial commodity could be made to flow spreading wealth into the rest of the economy. Derivatives of this view lie behind the emphasis on building steel plants in developing countries like India and on raising iron and steel output before all else in Communist countries. In the Eastern bloc in particular, the advance of heavy industry has taken priority over the interests of ordinary consumers.

In spite of the growing challenge of plastics there is no doubt even today that the iron and steel industry is still a commanding height of the economy and annual output is still anxiously watched by all politicians as a barometer of economic progress. Since the Russian revolution in 1917 the Soviet Union has slowly forced up its production and it now ranks close to the United States in total output. By 1951 Soviet output was second in the world at 32 million tons of crude steel and by 1965 the tonnage was over 90 million, only just behind the U.S. output of 118 million tons.

Clearly if Japan wanted to grow economically, the steel industry would have to be in the van and there would be grave problems to face. The first one was that Japan simply does not have any iron ore, and even home resources of coking coal are less than adequate. The second problem, arising from the first, was that expansion would involve heavy raw materials imports and therefore balance of payments difficulties.

In spite of these problems, which might well have caused some countries to give up altogether, Japan began to rebuild her steel industry after the war. Her performance is now widely known to have been fantastic. Firstly, her total production has risen slightly faster than that of Russia though Japan has only half the population. Secondly this growth has been achieved without the State pumping capital into the industry at the expense of other sectors. And thirdly the whole process has been accompanied by fierce competition between private firms without any moves towards State monopoly or nationalisation. In fact whilst the steel industry outpaced that of Russia and, of course, those of Britain, France, Germany and Italy, the Japanese consumer made no sacrifices whatsoever and consumed television sets (90 per cent of all households), refrigerators (62 per cent), and electric washing machines (75 per cent), to such an extent that these figures are even higher than in Western Europe. This tremendous expansion in steel output seems to have been more due to the pull of rising demand than to any other factor though sheer faith in Japan's everlasting boom has helped.

By the late 1970's it is very likely that Japan's steel output will actually exceed Russia's in absolute totals. This hard economic evidence may then go some way to shake the socialist planners' belief that heavy industry comes first and consumers last. Indeed the steel industry is an outstanding example of the way developments in Japan may confound accepted economic wisdom elsewhere in the world.

There are however some conventional explanations that can be given. For example one outstanding point is that Japanese capital investment has produced literally twice as much output as the equivalent amount invested by Britain over a comparable period. Japan has also had particularly good luck with her choices when faced with several technical options. A closer examination of these two points will go some way to explaining how Japan's economic miracle happened in this most important sector.

First it is necessary to explain that there is more to iron and steel making these days than used to be explained in school chemistry classes. In its essentials steelmaking has remained unchanged since the mid-nineteenth-century pioneers who invented the Bessemer and open hearth techniques. Stage one, practised for thousands of years, is to put iron ore and carbon with a bit of limestone into a furnace through which a blast of air can be blown. Hence the name 'blast furnace'. The carbon (it used to be charcoal but is now coke) reacts with the oxygen in the ore, and liberates impure iron which collects at the bottom in a molten state and is periodically tapped into a ladle. Stage two involves getting out of the iron the 7 or 8 per cent of impurities now dissolved in it. The Bessemer does this spectacularly by blasting air through the bottom of the molten metal; the carbon is burned out as carbon dioxide, other impurities dissolve in a floating slag, and if the blast is not switched off quickly enough the iron gets burned back to red iron oxide dust as well. That red cloud is one of the reasons for not living down-wind from a steel plant.

Whilst the Bessemer makes steel rapidly, the open hearth method may be said to simmer the iron until the impurities are removed; it makes better steel but cycle times for open hearth furnaces are very long, sometimes ten to fifteen hours.

Now in both cases it is oxygen which does the work of getting out impurities and in the early 1950s, in Austria, steelmakers started taking a short cut. Instead of using the oxygen contained in air they began to administer pure oxygen directly through a water-cooled lance or jet. The early experiments were carried out at Linz and Donawitz and these two towns gave their names to the LD method. Impure iron is poured into huge brick-lined steel pots mounted on swivels. The lances come down to within a few feet of the surface and blast pure oxygen at the metal turning 200 tons at a time into high quality steel. The 'blow' takes up to 25 minutes and cycle times or 'tap to tap' times can be as low as 32 minutes.

In 1967 the visitor to Japan could see over 60 of these converters installed and over 60 per cent of the total steel output was made this way. However, if one were to conclude that the low price and high quality of Japanese steel was entirely due to advanced technology one would be wrong; it is not so simple. A British steel baron, Sir Richard Summers, recently boasted that his old open hearth furnaces made cheaper steel than modern LD plants, and, unpopular though the remarks were, they were perfectly true in his case. There is far more to making cheap good steel than backing the right technical horse at the right time and the Japanese success is only partially explained by their immense investment in LD technology. To understand some of the other factors it is necessary to glance quickly back at the earlier history of the steel industry.

Before the Pacific War Japan's steel industry got pig iron and ore from Manchuria and coking coal from North China. During the Pacific War Government-encouraged development had expanded output to $7\frac{1}{2}$ million tons a year, with a further half million from Manchuria and Korea. The production came mainly from open hearth plants owned by one vast state company, Nippon Seitetsu, which, in the thirties, also controlled nearly all the blast furnaces in the country; this company then produced about half the ingot steel and two fifths of the rolled steel output, the various Zaibatsu produced the rest. After the Pacific War the Nippon Seitetsu was broken up and the old Yawata Company, itself once a Government creation in the 1900s, was given the lion's share; a new concern, Fuji Iron and Steel, got the rest, and the Government's shares were sold on the stock market.

By 1953 Yawata, Fuji and Nippon Kokkan (a tube producer before the War) produced about half the country's steel. The rest came from Sumitomo Metal Industries (ex-Zaibatsu and previously a non-ferrous metal specialist) Kawasaki Steel and Kobe Steel works. In addition there were many small companies which had previously worked on imported pig iron and these companies now began to specialise in rerolling steel and making steel from scrap.

So in the early fifties, Japan found herself with several large, vertically integrated producers and a multiplicity of very small companies. In terms of raw materials she had a diminishing flow of local coal of poor coking quality and a similarly unpromising supply of local ore which could not possibly provide the tonnages which were likely to be needed by the ambitious economic plans then in gestation. There was no alternative but to import and the Japanese set about the problem with characteristic energy.

The first problem was that importing coal and ore meant that transport costs would be higher than for most other nations. Coal had to come 10,000 miles from the East Coast of the United States and ore at least 7,000 miles from India or Australia. The first task was to reduce the costs by building very economical ships. Here the National Bulk Carrier philosophy of building ever bigger ships gained enthusiastic disciples. The fact that the cost of coking coal per ton of blast furnace iron was twice that in Germany or Britain just had to be tackled somehow. Cheaper sea transport was one way, more economical handling was another. There was obviously a premium on having as short a distance as possible between the berths of large ore ships and the blast furnaces. Hence coastal sites for steel plants were greatly in demand.

Unfortunately flat coastal sites were in demand for nearly everyone else, so Japanese steelmakers were driven to reclaiming land for steel plants from the sea.

The technique employed is to drive a curtain of steel piles into the sea bed, the landward side being formed by the original shore. The approach channel for bulk carriers which is usually up to 40 foot deep is then dredged out by cutter suction dredgers. These modern vessels are far removed from most people's idea of a typical dredger, the rusty old, steam-driven, ladder of buckets type seen close inshore in harbours. A modern cutter suction vessel, which may cost over a million pounds, disposes of its burden by piping the slurry from the sea bed to a prepared dumping ground, sometimes many miles away. In Japan the natural thing was to dredge out the channel for the ore ships and pipe the sand into the site selected for the steel plant.

Since the site is very cramped the planners are obliged to

squeeze as much capacity as possible into a very small area. This can mean that the actual capital cost of the plant may be very low almost by accident. That is to say that whereas in more fortunate countries planners may feel that the capital cost of a new plant built on green fields ought to come down a bit, in Japan it has been forced down a great deal because there is simply no land over which expensive roads and spacious factory building can be spread. This most unusual constraint leads to some remarkable comparisons. Kobe Steel at Nadahama produces 1.25 tons of steel a year for every square metre of the site, a recent (1961) British integrated plant, the Spencer Works of Richard Thomas and Baldwin produces 0.2 tons for every square metre, and some American plants are no better. Drawing up a world table on such a basis puts Japanese steel plants in all the top places. The fact that small and compact areas reduce internal hauls of materials and products to a minimum; that very few locomotives are needed; that little needs to be spent on foundations, internal railways and exchange sidings; all help to account for the astonishingly low capital cost of Japanese steel works. In the period of ten years from 1951 to 1961 the Japanese spent roughly the same amount as the British in capital investment (£1,100 million) and their steel capacity increased by twice as much, 28½ million tons compared to 13 million tons in Britain.

Another factor in the situation is that the Japanese are immune to a curious economic folly which particularly affects steel-makers in other countries; that is the practice of building for expansion. The British Spencer Works mentioned before are a particularly good example of this. The blast furnaces are capable of producing perhaps a half a million tons a year more of hot iron than the LD converters can turn into steel. The mill, which makes sheet, can handle from two to three times the tonnage produced by the blast furnace. Since a continuous strip and slabbing mill costs anything over £30 million, crude arithmetic suggests that at least £15 million of capital has been lying idle over the last eight years, to say nothing of the site preparation investment. In Japan a steelworks is planned to have a certain capacity and when complete, it runs at the target capacity. The capital invested is therefore made to produce at the maximum from the beginning whereas in many other countries plants are more expensive than their initial output merits. For the record the Spencer Works had accumulated a deficit of £25 million up to 1967.

There may be a good financial reason for the Japanese policy in that 10 or 11 per cent has to be paid on loan money. One drawback is that steel output tends to go up in quantum jumps of several million tons at a time, whereas in countries like Britain capacity is capable of being increased gradually. Nobody appears to have calculated just what this smooth increase of capacity costs to achieve so it may be concluded that the Japanese policy is probably the better. Furthermore since Japanese domestic demand is going up so fast, the embarrassment of excess capacity is not around for long enough to worry anybody except in times of rare recession.

But what about the technology? What other steps did the Japanese plan to offset the crippling handicap of having to import nearly all their raw materials?

One thing the Japanese began to do was to reduce as much as possible their coke consumption in the blast furnaces. According to the British Iron and Steel Institute, Japanese practice was achieving in 1953 average figures which were not reached in Britain until 1961. This low rate of consumption is due to judicious ore buying and the use of low sulphur American coke. One effect of good quality coke is that it provides less impurity to be taken out by slag; the less the volume of slag floating on the molten iron the less the heat wasted in keeping it molten. For the same object of keeping down slag, the Japanese spend a lot of time and trouble preparing the ore, and in general they try to keep blast furnaces running smoothly to fine margins. Another trick is to inject oil into the furnace which enables even less coke to be used. One blast furnace of the Osaka Iron and Steel Company has achieved world fame for its practice of injecting oil and oxygen, and steelmen seem to come from all over the world to admire its esoteric excellence.

It may readily be seen therefore that there are many more factors bearing on Japan's performance than the installation of those showcase LD furnaces.

Nevertheless there is still something inherently magnetic about LD furnaces because the whole life of a steel works is focused on them. In the melting shop there are generally two or three of them each about 30 feet in diameter and pivoted about 30 feet up in the air. They can be turned through 360° and are frequently turned upside-down to empty out slag. The cycle begins with charging a few tons of scrap steel to keep the temperature down when the molten iron is poured in later. Scrap may form up to 30 per cent of the charge but the amount to be used can be varied with great freedom. This factor is of great importance economically as will be seen later. Next a crane brings along a ladle of molten iron from the blast furnaces and pours this on the scrap. When the correct quantity has been charged the converter is tilted upright and the mouth is shrouded with a retractable hood. The oxygen lance is pushed down from above towards the metal and the 'blow' begins. The excess carbon in the impure blast-furnace iron is burned to carbon monoxide and this comes off as a gas. If the steelmaker wants a mild steel with say 0.3 per cent carbon in it he can get this by stopping the 'blow' at the right time. The practice is known as 'catching carbon' and is something that many British steelmakers pride themselves on being able to do. The Japanese seem to regard this practice as something that may interfere with production. If, for example, the 'blow' has been stopped too early then a second 'blow' may have to be undertaken and valuable minutes will have been wasted. Japanese practice is to 'blow' all the way to a very low carbon soft steel, and to adjust composition in the ladle after tapping. This is done by shovelling in the necessary corrective amounts of carbon, manganese, silicon and so on. Characteristically the important thing for them is to get maximum production at all costs. At Chiba works the two cranes that service the converters were so frequently exposed to the intense heat that their beams had begun to warp and bend. When someone mildly inquired what happened when the cranes broke down the manager gave the cranes what, on a Japanese face, passes for a baleful look and said, 'Break down? They wouldn't dare'.

Cranes keep going simply because they are intensively maintained by maintenance men who not only work the eight hour shift but hand over the job properly to the next shift by staying on long enough to overlap. In Britain the likelihood of crane breakdown is high enough for designers to play safe by putting in an extra crane as a backup; the penalty is not just the extra cost but as often as not a general slowdown. The reason is that it is often the middle of the three cranes which breaks down so there is no question of pushing it to the end of the shop for repair. Instead there is a complex game of ducks and drakes while ladles are manoeuvred past the out-of-action machine.

With LD furnaces as with nothing else, lost minutes really do count. The reason why so much attention is devoted to LD melting shop practice is that the relatively small converter vessels are virtually the valves which regulate the entire flow of resources in a vast steel plant. Anyone who goes to view the pair of active converters at Spencer Works in Britain can see the two narrow mouths through which flows almost a tenth of the whole country's steel output. This is a big contrast to open hearth furnaces which are so much less productive (although they may cost less) and are usually found in batches of twelve or even twenty. If something goes wrong with an open hearth furnace there may be ten hours in which to do something about it before the steel is ready, and even if it breaks down altogether one furnace contributes only a small proportion of total output. With LD converters, however, people go round with stopwatches: at one steel plant the tap-to-tap or cycle time was recently reduced by five minutes or so and output has gone up by half a million tons a year as a direct result.

An example of the determination to cut costs is provided by Yawata who have only two converters installed. Usually there are three and at any one time one of them will be out of action being relined. The one out of action is equipped with unproductive tilting motors, gas cleaning apparatus, oxygen lances and other service equipment and foundations. Yawata looked at the economics closely and decided it would be better to install fewer converters in a way which would allow them to be changed quickly. Consequently by a few modifications and the use of a converter carrier they can run a two-converter plant as productively as one half as big again of the conventional type.

When Japan began to embark on the LD spree in the late fifties it was not yet clear that the technology was going to achieve its present success. There were several other contenders for the job of efficient oxygen steelmaking, notably the Kaldo and Rotor processes, and the oxygen-assisted open hearth system was still in the fight. Japan did not choose LD entirely because of oriental cunning or the gift of prophecy. The important consideration was the availability of scrap.

In an old established industrial country like Britain half the annual output of steel comes from remelting and refining scrap and thus conventional open hearth techniques can still make economic sense if there is enough cheap scrap about (the raw material is much cheaper than hot metal from the blast furnace). Japan, however, had not been industrialised sufficiently long to be at the stage of consuming the machinery of the previous generation, and the projected rates of growth were too high. Japan was importing scrap at high prices in the fifties and LD technology provided the opportunity of making good steel without scrap or at least with very little. It also turned out that LD could make good steel of a wide range of composition in spite of dark forecasts that it would only be economical for low carbon soft sheet steel. The Japanese in 1963 claimed that the cost of LD steel ingots was 6 to 10 per cent less than from open hearth; by 1968 they were claiming reductions of 30 per cent.

It is arguable therefore that the Japanese have had a stroke of good luck with technological options. But, even without such luck, the surging economic growth of Japan has been rapid enough to encourage continuous expansion on a scale big enough for any mistakes to be quickly recovered.

The Japanese take great pains to avoid mistakes, but many features of their society could lead one to believe that they ought to be prone to making really very big ones. The paternalism of industrial society might lead one to believe that what the oldest captain of industry had to say was what clinched the argument. In reality they compensate for this by earnestly seeking the views of even the youngest men on the design of some new project. They are also the most avid data collectors it is possible to imagine and have an unnerving habit of copying down the most minor asides. At an OECD conference which took place shortly after Japan had joined the 'rich man's club' the writer witnessed a diverting example of this. At a dreary meeting in which a lot of political diplomats were saying nothing in lengthy platitudes about Scientific Manpower most people were drowsing gently, pretending to listen to the headphone translations. The Japanese came in and proceeded to take notes with tremendous animation and many hisses and whispers. Eventually more and more delegates woke up and began to listen to the speeches in utter bewilderment—what could it be that was so interesting? Perhaps they too ought to be paying attention. Soon a ripple of worry began to spread round the room. Although in this particular case the Japanese were wasting their time, their habit of data grubbing does often lead to wise choices well in advance of everybody else except the Americans.

Another reason why the Japanese steel industry avoids mistakes is its habit of maintaining close relations with the Universities. Steel is a glamour industry and it actually attracts science graduates. The head of Yawata's Fundamental Research Laboratory was previously a head of Tokio University. Technical education is much more orientated towards metallurgy and materials science than in the United Kingdom or France. In 1962, 1,190 degrees in metallurgy were awarded in Japan as against 255 in Britain at a time when their gross national products were of comparable size. Many Japanese universities have specialised research departments and there are also research institutes free of teaching responsibilities which specialise in specific limited fields like mineral dressing. Some of their work is done on a sponsored basis.

At the beginning of the chapter it was suggested that the

secret of the runaway steel industry lay in the pull of rising demand rather than in thrust of cheap production. The provision of good cheap steel has not been the driving force of Japanese economic growth, it has simply made that growth easier to achieve. It has done this in two ways, first by reducing the price of capital equipment for domestic use, second by generating direct and indirect exports which have helped to take the balance of payments strain.

The first role of the steel industry has been to pump out huge tonnages to the home market. The pattern of consumption reflects Japanese national priorities. The consumption of structural and mechanical engineering, shipbuilding and general manufacturing industry has increased well above the average rate since 1953 whilst that of gas, electricity and water utilities, rail transport and mining has grown less rapidly. Future rapid growth is predicted for motor body sheet, electrical machinery, silicon sheet and tinplate. The expressway building programme is already a large consumer of structural steel since Japanese expressways take to the air on stilts with far less fuss than in Britain. Japan, of course, is still building railways and this is another area of high consumption. The need to make buildings earthquake-proof has led to the construction of steel-framed blocks which use twice the amount of steel considered normal in more fortunate areas.

So far as the balance of payments is concerned raw materials are a sizeable debit item, but the steel industry's own direct exports of crude steel have usually been more than enough to offset it in the past. In some recent years there have been very large exports of crude steel and steel products helped along by large price cuts. 1966 figures show that Japan was the world's largest steel exporter if allowance is made for the fact that much of Germany's exports were inside the Coal and Steel Community. The export target reached in 1965 was ten million tons. Direct steel exports account for around 15 per cent of Japan's total export trade but the imported raw materials bill in 1967 was as high as $1,700 million. Exports now need to be well over 10 million tons to reduce an expected deficit of $260 million in

1967. Indirect steel exports also pull their weight, because between 10 and 15 per cent of home-consumed steel ends up in goods which are exported. The shipbuilding industry is, of course, outstanding as a huge consumer of steel which eventually finishes up as a foreign exchange earner.

Can the steel industry go on booming? In spite of a current capacity that leaves observers incredulous, the steel bosses are still engaging in a war of expansion to find out who loses his nerve first. Presently the competition centres on who will build the biggest blast furnace. The current fashion decrees that an integrated steel plant ought to produce around 6 million tons a year (at least twice the favoured production for West European units) so Yawata led off with a new monster blast furnace over 2,000 cu. ft. in capacity in 1967. MITI set up a special committee to regularise affairs but there has been little to suggest that its restraining influence has been effective. Fuji, Kawasaki and Nippon Kokkan had all started their big new blast furnaces in early 1968. Since other companies are terrified of losing their market shares they are rushing in as well. Sumitomo are determined to have a blast furnace of 2,700 cu. ft. capacity. The stage will then no doubt be set for the thrilling competition of who will build the world's first 3,000 cu. ft. blast furnace. By this time Japan will have already sailed past the 77 million ton mark.

This, say Japan's planners unhappily, must lead to 'a deflationary gap', that is excess capacity.

Put this view to the steel industry, and you get this sort of argument in reply. First, 'Although we felt a bit worried in the 1964–65 recession, it now seems clear that Japan is going straight up to a West European standard of life. West Germany, with a population of 60 million, produces 40 million tons of steel a year, so Japan with a population of 100 million should produce over 70 million tons.' Since Japan's steel output per head had already exceeded Britain's in 1967 that leaves one a little breathless. Secondly, and of more immediate economic relevance, 'Japan has discovered that it can export competitively to the United States. Our technology has caught up with theirs, and our wage costs are lower.' This is exactly what the steel protection lobby is saying in the United States, adding that since American labour productivity is much higher, there is nothing else the industry can do but demand a quota limit on Japanese exporters. By 1968 Japanese industrialists were promising their US counterparts that they would export in an 'orderly fashion' but since their products sell for $10 to $15 a ton less than that of their American counterparts the discipline seems to lie with the customers.

Thirdly, it seems fairly likely that the companies bringing forward their investment programmes fastest just hope that the others won't follow.

In 1968 Yawata, the biggest company, proposed to merge with Fuji, the second biggest, thus creating the third largest steel company in the world and one which would be responsible for nearly one third of total Japanese output. MITI is reported to approve the merger for two reasons. One is probably that it will allow the Government more control but the second reason is that Japan will now be able to allow foreign capital into the industry, secure in the knowledge that nobody can buy out a giant that big. The next event in this story of colossal expansion will almost certainly be the world number one position for Yawata-Fuji since US Steel's annual output at 28 million tons (current biggest) is only 6 million tons ahead and the Japanese firms are both growing more rapidly.

Japan's steel industry thus presents a remarkable picture. It is a long way from classic capitalistic enterprises and such niceties as being cautious with the shareholders' money, but it is equally far from the State-sponsored steel industries being built in socialist countries behind the Iron Curtain. It has been more successful than either.

TEN

Railways in the Golden Age

In Japan the Golden Age of Railways lingers on. What is basically a nineteenth-century concept of transport is in full health, humming with the best of twentieth-century technology. The railways are probably the only reason that anyone addicted to nostalgia would pay Japan a special visit. The trains are clean and tidy, they are punctual literally to the second, a Japanese version of Bradshaw still gives that special pleasure to the leisured enthusiast, branch lines still wind into the distant valleys and there, even at the smallest village halt, a station-master is still somebody special.

It gives the Western visitor a slight feeling of being outside of time when, at a business meeting in some ultra modern glass and concrete office block, the train timetable is produced as a prelude to action. At first one has a feeling of irritation that business life must revolve around train times, that one must be forever reserving seats and booking tickets, but after a while the discipline becomes less irksome, and anyway, everybody else goes by train. Ten years ago a journey from Tokyo to Osaka by motor car was almost as much an adventure as it was in Commodore Perry's time. The Tokaido road, the traditional route between the two great cities, was more like a building contractor's access road and the general level of hazard was so great that on arrival at journey's end it was customary, even mandatory, to ring up and assure your friends that you had actually made it.

Until very recently therefore there was no question of moving about Japan except by rail, so the railways occupied a central role in economic life and were never regarded, as they are in the United States and Britain, as a worn-out, old-fashioned, money-losing mess. Oddly enough Japanese railways do lose money, much of the rolling stock is old-fashioned and a good deal of the equipment is worn out. Apart from this, morale on the railways could not be higher. Japan's pride and joy, the New Tokaido Line (NTL), deserves its world-wide fame and, far from being the final defiant glorious gesture before the motor car and the expressway make the railway obsolete, is to be the beginning of a new 2,400 mile network to link the principal cities of Japan. Are the Japanese mad? Or do they mean to leap the motor car age, anticipate the coming of the megalopolis and install the sort of modern railway that some experts are beginning to think will be the only answer to medium and short haul transport problems in the future?

The Japanese themselves do not all think in those terms although some of the planners and the railway management do. In the recent past Japan's railway policy has really been based on immediate responses to the facts of life as they appeared and almost by accident the policy which resulted turned out to have been ideally economic from the national point of view. One reason for this is that the two kinds of railway, commuter and inter-city, have been owned by separate bodies; another is that Japan is ideally suited to railways by virtue of its geography.

About 70 per cent of the Japanese land area is mountainous and the flat areas are mainly narrow strips along the coast or valleys, fingering up into the mountainous interior. Since the population is high, agricultural land has to be intensively cultivated and conserved; therefore the urban areas are very crowded. As industrialisation proceeds, traffic demands have risen steeply but usually along a few simple axes dictated by the lie of the land. A city like Los Angeles in which over half the area is roadway would be inconceivable in central Japan, unless it was a double-decker city. Space for new motorways is very limited and costs are high because they often have to be elevated. The ordinary trunk roads passing through built-up areas are narrow and sinuous. Even when Japan is solidly in the motor age, all these factors mean that railways will still be relatively better off than in countries with more space. Furthermore in most other developed countries the rise of the motorcar has been gradual and the period during which the railways have suffered decline has been correspondingly long. If a resurgence does come for example in the United States 'North East corridor' from Boston to New York to Washington, it will come to a railway system demoralised by twenty to thirty years of contraction and unprofitability. The resurgence, of course, comes because the motorcar chokes the roads so much that the basic convenience of the private car is completely offset by the uncertainty of journey times and the difficulty of parking. Since Japan is due to get 30 million cars on the roads by 1980 and since parking is already as difficult as in Paris or Rome, the period in which railways are forsaken by passengers is likely to be short. Indeed if the New Tokaido Line's success is anything to go by, Japan may bypass this stage altogether. So far as freight is concerned, conventional services have never fallen to the level of British Rail's, and the Japanese are even celebrating the carriage of the first marine containers straight from the docks.

However one of the most unusual features of Japanese railways is the fact that privately-owned railways co-exist with the nationalised network and have taken much of the burden of commuter services. Tokyo or any other big city in the rush hour has to be experienced to be believed, but most people will have seen pictures of the pushers who pack the passengers into the commuter trains.

JNR runs commuter services too, but half of the lines are privately owned, either by independent public companies, private companies, or municipalities. One effect of this division has been to let JNR concentrate more on inter-city developments often undertaken with government money, whilst the commuter lines have lived in a crueller and more commercial world. These private railways have survived only by intensively exploiting their assets in a most remarkable way and new investment has not necessarily been in railroad hardware. Some of the enterprise has taken forms which would shock the railwaymen of other countries where running a railway is interpreted more narrowly.

Takarazuka is a Japanese village full of cherry blossom which has a zoo and the most famous collection of girls in Japan. It owes its fame to a railway baron who decided that in order to increase the utilisation of his commuter line into Osaka, the distant rural end had better be given some sort of attraction. So he established the Takarazuka Girls' Opera Theatre just beyond the terminus of his line. It is housed in a separate enormous building a short walk across the station courtyard. The performances, which are one of Japan's tourist attractions, are an inexplicable mixture of melodrama, song and dance, circus (with animals) classical drama and movie show pastiche. The girls are chosen as the most beautiful in Japan and no male actors are to be seen. The auditorium is vast, seating 3,000 and the tickets are no more than ten shillings a head. The place is usually packed with schoolgirls who idolise the actresses.

So famous is this extraordinary girl opera that one actually gets the feeling that the railway was built to get to it whereas in truth, Takarazuka was built to give the railway somewhere to go.

Private railways will do almost anything to keep their wheels rolling outside the peak commuter hours. Recreation grounds, ball parks, sports stadia, bathing resorts and floral gardens are all on the list and where a line happens to pass through especially pretty countryside, there are usually 'Romance' expresses which run on national holidays or weekends. Since the private lines often run together between the same place (there are three for example between Kobe and Osaka) competition between them is vicious, particularly on holidays. The competition takes the form of providing luxurious observation trains with very good steward service. All manner of refreshments can be bought and there is a particularly delightful provision of hot face-towels sealed in individual plastic bags. As the train pulls out of the station, there is always the sound of sporadic claps as passengers bang the plastic bags between their palms to liberate the railway company's hot towels.

Railway companies have also sought to attract passengers by real estate developments along their routes and the low standard of some of these railway houses has drawn much unfavourable comment. Although it is customary to excuse this by saying that the Japanese do not regard houses, traditionally made of wood and paper, in quite the same way as old-fashioned West Europeans whose homes are their castles, where Western-style flats are on offer they are oversubscribed many times. The shopper has been another target for exploitation and the most staggering thing any traveller notices in Japan is the massive size of the department stores built on the site of downtown rail terminals; Harrods or Macy's would fit twice over into some of them and they represent very profitable investments indeed. As discussed in Chapter 6 they operate quite outside the big bankers' control and will sell anything from a light aircraft to a kimono or an Old Etonian English tie. On the roof there is often a Japanese garden centre where you can buy 'instant roots' like ancestral carp with plastic ponds, ancient stone lanterns (very expensive indeed, these), bonsai trees and accidentally artistic-looking rocks. The shopper from the suburbs need never set foot in Tokyo city. In fact, except for jobs, the private railways can provide a cradle-to-grave service; people can buy and live in their houses, go to the station in the railway company's buses, travel in the train, shop at the department stores and super-markets, play games on the recreation grounds and go to the other end of the line for a holiday staying in a railway company hotel. The contrast with the decrepit commuter railways on Long Island on the American East Coast, or the London sub-urban lines which end in seedy Victorian terminals on priceless sites like Marylebone or Cannon Street, could not be more marked.

Is it so unreasonable for a railway company to maximise the return on the resources it has? Does it really hurt if a huge office block or department store, or even both together, spring up on top of a railway terminal, to the benefit of the railway and its customers? For reasons best known to themselves city authori-ties elsewhere in the world have chosen to regard railways as being responsible only for running trains. Meanwhile architects and town planners labour to invent new towns which eventually turn out to be linear in shape with a railway running down the middle and shopping centres on the terminals.

Whatever the ultimate merits or demerits of the private commuter railways, the point is that they have taken care of themselves and the nationalised JNR has been left free to concentrate more on inter-city travel and freight. Perhaps at this point, it would be as well to relate how the present situation arose.

Like nearly everything else in modern Japan the railways started in 1868 after the Meiji Restoration in Tokyo. The first line, built with the help of the British, went to Yokohama and the first Tokaido line reached Osaka in 1889. It was Government owned but the financial strain was high and private building was encouraged. This boomed so fast that by 1892 private lines were over twice as long as those of the central Government and a 'Railway Construction Law' was passed to control them. In the early part of this century an industrial recession hit them badly and the Government nationalised 4,400 km. of them in 1906 and 1907. Modernisation began in the 1920s when many lines were electrified and automatic coupling was introduced. During the Pacific War more private lines were nationalised. As in other countries, rolling stock was badly run down and the railways were losing money. The Korean War gave JNR a fillip and from 1957 onwards tremendous expansion has been undertaken in a series of five year plans. In 1965 JNR carried 45 per cent of all passenger kilometres travelled in Japan including about 21 per cent of commuter traffic. The private railways carried about an equal amount of commuter traffic but virtually no freight.

Constitutionally JNR comes under the Ministry of Transport and it submits to the scrutiny of the Government's audit board. The President of JNR is appointed by the Cabinet and he presents his budget to the Diet itself. JNR's current assets, operating 20,000 route kilometres throughout Japan, are worth 2.4 million yen and the Third Long Range Plan (1965–71) calls for the spending of 2.9 million yen thereby effectively doubling the railway system in six years. These heady investment figures are of course characteristically Japanese; expansion comes first. One thing Japanese railways are determined to do is to hold on to their share of the nation's transport demand.

Certainly JNR's commuter services just have to expand because, as with the private railways, current capacity is grossly overloaded. The Japanese have it expressed in precise statistics as usual. 'The Central Line in Tokyo,' a JNR official explained, 'is operated by one train with ten cars every two minutes. The capacity of one car is 144, comprised of 54 seated and 90 standing passengers. That is 1,440 persons per train. The congestion limit recently reached 2.8. That is 3,232 passengers actually travel on the train.' In human terms this means that one simply cannot lift one's arms, or sometimes even turn one's head.

Let us turn away from the insoluble problem of the commuter. There is no doubt that the railways will continue to be the only safe, sure way of handling this problem, even if they do have to build double decker tracks. The future of the commuter railways is not in doubt in Tokyo or any other large city. What is in doubt is the future of the railways as inter-city passenger carriers and freight carriers and here JNR is a world leader.

The figures show that private cars and buses are slowly eating into JNR's share of passenger traffic and that trucks are doing the same to freight, but the absolute demand for passenger and freight services goes on rising every year. Hence because of Japan's steadily booming economy the railway system, although suffering a relative decline, is nevertheless expanding fast.

This is a most important point because it means that the atmosphere in which the management operates is very different from that in most other developed countries where railways are contracting in absolute terms. The JNR management has much more room to manoeuvre and is concerned to redeploy to meet demand rather than cut back to reduce losses. Nevertheless some familiar news was recently published. Towards the end of 1967 JNR asked the Government to raise commuter fares and to abolish the need to pay taxes to local governments. It also announced that it was contemplating the closure of 6,000 km. of unprofitable lines. It transpired that only 14 out of 242 lines showed a profit in 1966. Among the profitable ones was, of course, the Tokaido line. All the familiar palliatives were being applied from diesel rail buses to automatic crossing gates, from closing stations to operating alternative buses by road. Ultimately, JNR feel that loss-making lines must be separately accounted and if the Government wants to keep them going it must pay the difference. Obviously some of the losses must be due to rural depopulation but others show that Japan is not immune to the familiar railway diseases. What is not yet clear is how much railway fares can rise before provoking a switch to other forms of transport. The safest place to raise fares is on commuter lines because such a switch is impossible.

Let us turn to the expansion plans, bearing in mind that profitability is only loosely related to the decision as to whether to expand or not. Expansion will take place first where demand is greatest and the railway planners are under no illusions as to what will happen if they do not meet the demands. Up to 1961 the amount of freight actually awaiting shipment at stations often exceeded two million tons, and with improved road conditions truck transport was making big inroads. Since 1963 JNR has fought back hard. Its share of freight transport was 38 per cent in 1960 and 30 per cent in 1966 but during that period the absolute volume had gone up by about 6 per cent. Apart from conventional measures to improve the service JNR established rapid transport and container services.

Between 1966 and 1968 the number of containers was more than doubled up to 24,000, and 100,000 are planned by 1971. All the containers are made of steel and painted light green. They are all the same rather small size with a capacity of five tons. Handling is usually by fork-lift truck and JNR boast that special care is taken to avoid tilting them. The container service is door-to-door since JNR owns its own trucks which take the freight to and from the stations. JNR's standard container is about half the size of the 8 × 8 × 20 foot marine container and they have taken to manufacturing special flat wagons suitable for either. Container terminals are already in operation at Tokyo and Kobe with Osaka and Yokohama due to be complete by 1970. It is expected that about 50 per cent of the goods moved between Japan and the United States will be containerised by 1970 so this link-up with major ports is important.

The container trains operate separately from normal freight and bypass the marshalling yards. So far the nationwide freightliner service with special terminals on the style of British Rail's has not yet been developed. Container wagons are coupled to limited express freight trains and enjoy a general priority, but only between Tokyo and Osaka are there trains exclusively devoted to containers. For freight JNR emphasise not only speed in handling but speed in transit and, as with British Rail, 70 to 80 m.p.h. averages are the ultimate target.

Although the Japanese have visited Britain to look at freight liners, the whole world has visited Japan to look at passenger trains, in particular to look at the New Tokaido Line. This is without doubt the finest passenger service in the world and has made railways all over Europe and America think again about the possibilities of arresting their own decline.

Many writers, film directors and photographers have tried hard to communicate the essence of a ride on the NTL and most of them have failed. The main reason is that the ride is so smooth that even 130 m.p.h. feels comfortable. The scenery swings past quickly but the NTL rides high on embankments and the view doesn't give very much impression of speed. The trains are tall off the ground, so even filmed from the outside there's little impression of real speed. Furthermore, it's uncommonly difficult to convey a feeling of power, because there is no muscle-bound hauling locomotive at the front as on European and British trains. Instead each axle of each car is individually powered, the whole train starts as one without any jerk. The only visual impression of high speed comes when two trains pass each other in opposite directions. The best word to describe the motion was picked by Australian travel writer Colin Simpson, who describes the train as 'slithering' and somehow that is exactly it.

The New Tokaido Line was born of necessity when the Japanese railways were undeniably at their zenith. The area along the ancient Tokaido highway from Osaka to Tokyo contains 40 per cent of Japan's population, and these people produce 70 per cent of her total industrial output. The old narrow-gauge Tokaido Line (3' 6") was just one long bottleneck and quite incapable of meeting rising demands even in the fifties so the railway planners decided on a brand new ultra-high-speed double track standard gauge railway, the first 4' 8½" railway in Japan. When the project was first announced the planners were either regarded as 'fantastic visionaries' or as madmen. The whole idea was a *folie de grandeur*, especially the budget – 380,000 million yen (£400 million, or $1,000 million).

JNR raised the money somehow, mainly in the form of government loans, but they also raised money from the World Bank. Construction began in 1959 and the railway took its first fare-paying passengers in October 1964, five and a half years later.

The New Tokaido Line is not so much a technological feat as an act of fiscal courage. Most of its features can be found elsewhere in the world, and French trains have run even faster on test. The really astounding thing is that the railway dared to take the plunge and build all 320 miles of it. The rail bed itself had to be especially free from bumps and twists. In order to keep the radius of the bends as great as possible many new tunnels had to be bored and extra headroom was necessary to accommodate the air-pressure wave caused by the high speed. 13 per cent of the line is tunnelling and 4 per cent is bridging; nearly a fifth of the total mileage is elevated. There was no question of level crossings, so long embankments were built to clear highways by up to 20 feet, (a wise decision, as the British experience of level-crossing accidents has demonstrated). New stations were built, twelve for passengers and four for freight with two new electric railcar bases. The track itself was welded steel rail on rubber pads, set in pre-stressed concrete sleepers. The whole track is designed to be continuously replaced on a ten year cycle.

Automatic train control was also essential and the operation of the whole line is now controlled centrally from Tokyo. Circuits laid in the track transmit speed instructions into the train as it runs over them and the information is presented in the driver's cab. If the driver does not respond, the train's speed is automatically reduced. All the driver really has to do is to stop the train on the right spot at the stations. Radio telephony is also installed so that the business man can keep in touch in case the three-hour journey is too long. The trains are electrically powered picking up 25 KV from overhead wires with each axle under drive. At present the line is worked from six in the morning until midnight with maintenance occupying the intervening hours. Irregularities in the track are detected by inspection cars which are specially constructed to do their job fast. In fact the inspection cars can cover the whole track from Tokyo to Osaka in one night when hauled by a 130 m.p.h. diesel service locomotive.

Since Japan is periodically assailed by typhoons and earthquakes the track is provided with anemometers and seismographs. If either instrument reads too high or stops transmitting because of genuine disaster all trains are brought to a halt. Another strange feature, unique to the Tokaido line, is its own power supply. The need for this arises from the fact that one half of Japan runs at 60 cycles frequency, the other at 50 cycles. Making the trains run on both frequencies would have raised the weight by over two tons per car so JNR provided a private grid supply for about 170 km. of the track out of Tokyo. They had to build a private frequency-converter station which takes in power at 50 cycles, drives an electric motor which in turn drives a generator producing alternating current at 60 cycles. This current is then fed down the line by a string of substations.

When the NTL began to operate, the worst forebodings of its critics seemed to be confirmed. It was said to be making a loss; any hope of paying back the capital, even in forty years, seemed remote. Airline competition was serious; it still took four hours from Osaka to Tokyo. Dark rumours circulated about the train wheels; they were wearing out so quickly that they had to be reground every night. But gradually the NTL stepped up the pace and began to solve its problems. The Kodama (The Echo) and the Hikari (Lightning, the faster of the two services) picked up speed, punctuality, and passengers. The time between Tokyo and Osaka came down to 3 hours 10 minutes, and the NTL's reputation began to spread. It became as smart to take the new train as to fly and eventually even smarter. The New Tokaido was unique, anybody could fly but the world's fastest and most glamorous train was something special. It was air-conditioned and double-glazed. There were spacious reclining seats, buffet cars, public telephones, three face mirrors in the lavatories and soothing music in the air. It became favoured by honeymoon couples, and any afternoon at the weekends you will see at least half a dozen wedding parties at the big stations. It is certainly favoured by business-men; currently over four million passengers a month are being carried and the New Tokaido Line is 'in the black'. £8 million half-yearly profit in 1967! There is even talk that it will pay back its capital in ten years which, even if it doesn't give it the sort of profitability enjoyed by a new ski-lift, is enough to cause amazement amongst the rest of the world's railways. It's not as if it is the only service between Osaka and Tokyo either; the basic fare is nearly double what it would cost by the old Tokaido line so people could, if they wanted to, travel much more cheaply, and poorer people probably do. The fares are comparable with those charged on British Rail, and the first class fare by Hikari is about the same as the air fare, about £7. 5s. 0d. for 310 miles. Significantly the airline's share of the Osaka-Tokyo traffic has fallen from 14.6 per cent when the NTL opened to 5.7 per cent in 1967. As Japan goes on getting prosperous the traffic goes on rising; already average load factors are up to 90 per cent.

It would be uncharacteristic of the Japanese if they were to call it a day with this great success. Already the New Tokaido Line is being extended towards Hiroshima as the San Yo Line and the next section, ending at Okayama, is due to be completed by 1972. Later fast freight services on especially designed rolling stock are to be introduced. They will certainly have to be fast to keep out of the way of the money-spinning passenger trains. Beyond this JNR intend to take the New Tokaido Line right round the country by building 2,500 more miles of track. The cost will be between four and five thousand million pounds at today's prices and the line will link Nagasaki at one end of Japan to Sapporo, up in the Northern island of Hokkaido at the other. Journey times to Sapporo, at present nineteen hours, will be reduced to just under six hours. The project also involves, apparently in passing, a Japanese version of the Channel Tunnel 22 miles long under the Tsugaru Straits between Hokkaido and the main island of Honshu. The designed maximum speed will be up to 157 m.p.h. so the old New Tokaido Line will seem slow by comparison. Not that the Japanese haven't thought of this as well; a new New Tokaido Line will be built inland of the present one they say, thus freeing the original New Tokaido Line for more high speed freight. The New New Tokaido will do Osaka in 2 hours 30 minutes which, unless airports revolutionise themselves, will leave the railway in command in the foreseeable future.

This grandiose trunk plan came in response to an initiative from the Liberal Democratic Party (the present Government) which set up a City Policy Deliberation Council. This Council had asked JNR for a plan to stimulate local economic development by reducing journey times between cities in 1966, and if JNR's plan goes forward it will bring areas 300 miles apart as close together as some New York or London suburbs are today.

In addition to this JNR also plan to take on 48 more regional development lines at present being worked up by a body called the Japan Railway Construction Corporation (JRCC). This group was created in 1964 to relieve JNR of the burden of building the 3' 6" narrow-gauge lines itself and is occupied in doubling tracks and electrifying lines. About 34 per cent of Japan's lines will be electrified by 1971 and the last steam locomotives will be banished by 1975. Diesels will haul the rest of the traffic. In the research laboratories work continues on the world's largest linear motor, a sort of electric motor rolled flat which has no moving parts to set up friction. Anticipating the high cost of track maintenance labour, JNR have also produced a track that needs no attention for five years.

If the reader is now reeling from a deluge of expansionist statistics and development plans, one can only explain that is just how it seems to anyone who visits Japan. Whether JNR are realistic or not in view of the current deficits is not easy to judge but the Japanese do not talk about economic infrastructure without having done their sums. They see the railways as providing this vital infrastructure and it may well be that they will put up with some deficits on a regular basis. They are now working out the economics of individual lines in order to judge the need for closures of unprofitable ones. But the real reason that JNR's deficits draw less hostility than those of say British Rail or German Railways is simply that JNR run a good railway – clean, punctual and very fast. In the coming years it will be interesting to see if the golden age continues. At least the railways will not sink so low in public esteem that they will have to be renamed, as in the United States, 'duorails' before they can get the passengers back on board.

ELEVEN

Chemicals and the Government

Any account of Japan's economic miracle has to deal with the chemical industry because this is one of the fundamental features of any modern industrialised nation.

Probably no industry is subject to so much government intervention anywhere else in the world, except in communist countries. And strange to say, probably no industry has grown quite so fast even in Japan. These remarks apply to petrochemicals of course, not to the old established processes for making bulk chlorine, sulphuric acid and the other inorganic commodity chemicals. All plans for expansion in petrochemicals must be approved by the Ministry of International Trade and Industry (MITI) under laws passed in 1957 and 1962. This complete control arose from the need to rationalise the industry which was growing up as many fragmented companies. The need to rationalise came from the fact that most of these little Japanese companies would have been engulfed by the oil companies which are frequently half American owned. MITI was also concerned about overall efficiency but, even so, this complete control can have few parallels elsewhere in the free world. It is even stricter than the arrangement in the British Iron and Steel Industry where the industry's own board (before nationalisation) had to vet expansion plans but only if they exceeded £100,000 in capital value. In Japan MITI looks into everything, nothing is excluded.

In spite of, or even because of this, the growth in petrochemicals has been staggering. Production value rose from about

£11 million in 1958 to £240 million in 1964, and in that latter year the expansion rate was an astonishing 33 per cent. For the chemical industry as a whole, taking 1960 as a base year at 100, the production index by 1965 had gone up to 211; for petrochemicals by themselves it was 662.

Another extraordinary feature is the huge output of PVC or polyvinylchloride. Although the total Japanese chemical output has a good way to go before equalling that of the United Kingdom or West Germany, the output of PVC is already three times that of Britain and amounts to 600,000 tons a year. It's difficult to say where it all goes but Japanese agriculture appears to account for a good deal. PVC film is popular for mulching rice paddies and horticultural crops such as strawberries. (Mulching is covering the ground with a damp dark layer to bring on germination and early growth). Transparent PVC is also used in agriculture for making temporary glasshouses. The building industry is another great outlet where water supply and mains sewerage are often in PVC. Because Japan works on a lower voltage than Britain, electrical conduit need not be so stout, so again PVC is used. Furthermore, since earthquake-prone Japan has a tradition of flimsy house construction, PVC panels have found a ready market as roofing and floor material. PVC accounts for about half the total tonnage of the plastics industry. About 20 per cent of the total output goes to export and Japanese know-how is so good that the technology is being exported too. Joint ventures are being set up in Portugal, Australia, Trinidad, Venezuela and other Latin American countries.

There are other sectors of the plastics field in which Japan is a world leader and one of them, the synthetic leather industry, is particularly interesting. Success in this difficult field is a very good measure of the quality of a nation's chemists. Before looking at this specialised field however it is necessary to sketch in something of the history of the chemical industry as a whole.

Japan's own sources of raw materials are somewhat limited to say the least. Coal, limestone, hydroelectricity and a little gypsum just about complete the list, although natural gas has recently been discovered at Niigata. Before the war, therefore, calcium carbide, made from coke and limestone, had to be the basic chemical feedstock. Japan is still the world's largest producer with a total of 2.2 million tons but a good deal of this capacity is now unemployed and a lack of growth is widely apparent. Most of the products that came from calcium carbide through acetylene can be made more economically from the naphtha fraction of petroleum. The petrochemical industry has therefore supplied most of the increases in general demand in recent years. Japan has to import all the phosphate rock needed for fertiliser, all her salt and sulphur. Other imports include bauxite and alumina, potassium chloride, crude rubber, titanium ore, and of course crude oil.

Before petrochemicals began to boom the Japanese chemical industry was securely tucked under the wings of the ex-Zaibatsu groups Sumitomo, Mitsubishi and Mitsui. Even today the biggest chemical company is still Sumitomo Chemical, employing 12,000 workers. Its products range from ammonia through caustic soda, chlorine, calcium carbide, urea, to PVC pharmaceuticals and dyestuffs. Mitsubishi is the second biggest company making a similar range of products. These companies are typical of the original enterprises producing fertilisers and industrial chemicals from coal, limestone, pyrites and salt.

When the petrochemical boom started the old pattern was swiftly altered. Oil companies like Nippon Oil, Toa Neuryo and Maruzen built cracking facilities either alone or in co-operation with smaller chemical companies. Mitsui and Mitsubishi set up their own petrochemical subsidiaries, and then Mitsui Chemical and Toyo Koatsu jumped on the bandwaggon as well. Soon Mitsui and Mitsubishi will have rival petrochemical complexes within the same group. In all there are nine separate locations for petrochemical activity and their main concern is to supply cracker chemicals to other chemical companies. Vertical integration, on the style of the ICI Teeside plants which start with oil and end up with nylon, polypropylene etc., is rare. It is small wonder that MITI has felt the need to rationalise the situation. Here is one example of the web, which starts with Mitsui Petrochemical's big centre at Iwakuni-Ohtake producing 160,000 tons of ethylene per year. The company was established in 1955 by the Mitsui group and it began to function in 1958 on naphtha supplied by Koa Oil. California Texas Oil owns 50% of Koa, and Koa owns 10% of Mitsui Petrochemical. Products include polyethylene, ethylene oxide, glycol, acetaldehyde and acrylonitrile. Much of the ethylene goes to Mitsui Polychemical which is a joint company set up by Mitsui Petrochemical and Du Pont for manufacturing low-density polyethylene and propylene. The latter goes to yet another multiple owner company to make polypropylene. It would be surprising if the Americans could ever sort out just what their stake in all this actually amounted to. Even if they did they would still find it pretty difficult to repatriate the profits.

One of the success stories for homegrown Japanese technology is Toyo Koatsu's urea process which has been widely licensed abroad. Like much Japanese technology it is not startlingly original in conception; it is however a brilliant optimisation of all the individual processes linked together.

Urea's first claim to fame is that it was the first organic chemical ever to be made from inorganic matter. The trick was done by Wöhler in 1828 and helped to demolish the idea that organic chemicals embodied some sort of vital force and could only be derived from animate material. Its importance in the modern world lies in the fact that it is both a very efficient fertilizer and a starting point for a family of valuable plastics.

In the soil it breaks down into ammonia and carbon dioxide and therefore produces assimilable nitrogen for plants. So does its main rival, ammonium sulphate, but in this case the proportion by weight of nitrogen is much less. Since transport costs loom large in fertilizer economics there was a strong motive to make the production of urea as efficient as possible, especially in view of the Japanese Government's determination to try to make the country agriculturally self-sufficient.

The principle of urea production is simple. Ammonia and carbon dioxide are pumped into a reactor at 180°C and 200 atmospheres pressure. They react, and urea is produced. The first problem is that the initial mixture of gases is very corrosive and causes rapid wear at the pumps. The second problem is that extra ammonia is needed to improve the yield of urea but it is difficult to recover from the resulting gas mixture. The old process was to turn the excess ammonia into ammonium sulphate but economic demand for this was falling. Meanwhile the demand for urea was going up. After many years of continuous development effort, Toyo Koatsu scientists produced a very efficient plant design in which there is great economy in the use of raw materials.

Other notable Japanese processes display similar virtues of high efficiency and economy and much of the research effort has gone into process development rather than into inventing wholly new products. Kureha Chemicals' 'mixed gas' process is a nice example. This starts with naphtha from the oil refineries which is cracked rather easily into a mixture of acetylene and ethylene. Instead of trying to separate these gases or improve the yield of ethylene, the Japanese have looked at the end products desired. As will be apparent from the figures quoted for PVC output, vinyl chloride is one of the most desirable of these products. The mixture of gases is therefore reacted with chlorine, and the ethylene goes straight to vinyl chloride. A by-product of this reaction is hydrochloric acid, and this is in turn used to treat the acetylene. The product is again vinyl chloride which is now all led off to be polymerised into polyvinyl chloride. The whole process is a model of economy and is now computer-controlled.

Western observers notice similar attention to economic detail in the manufacture of chlorine from imported salt. The know-how was bought before the war but steady development effort has resulted in running the normal brine cells at higher and higher current densities and at increased temperatures. This was one of the earliest examples of squeezing the best out of imported technology.

Much of the conventional chemical industry exists in order to provide materials for other industrial processes but the plastics industry is quite different. It makes materials which are used in their own right, and as the skill of the chemist improves, so the competitive power of man-made materials threatens not only non-ferrous metals but even iron and steel as well.

Take, for example, the use of plastics in the motor car industry. In this area plastics are on the frontiers of a massive breakthrough even in stagnant Britain. The argument goes like this. Plastics are rustless, they have a high stiffness to weight ratio and they do not need expensive finishing in paint shops. Steel sheet costs say 26 pence per pound, when it has been pressed into panel form. Polypropylene costs 43 pence per pound weight of panel but because it has superior stiffness this extra cost is offset. Measured in terms of pence per square foot of equally stiff panel the price for steel is about 31 pence, for ABS plastic 41 pence, and for polypropylene 31 pence. On this basis therefore plastics are already threatening steel.

Now, as technology advances and plastic production plants grow bigger, the cost of plastics tends to fall. For steel, on the other hand, because energy costs tend to rise, the opposite is the case. What holds up the inevitable?

In Britain the answer is both conservative managements and the need to write off heavy investment in conventional technology. Since the rate of expansion of vehicle output is so low the opportunity to put in new plant occurs infrequently. In Japan, however, the car industry is developing at a very high rate under technically adventurous managements. At Toyo Kogyo, as already mentioned, the engineer bosses have installed computers in every possible place and have backed advanced technology like the Wankel engine. The attractions of plastic cars which, by being lighter will have smaller engines, better acceleration and so on, will need no stressing for them. Honda already has plastic panels in production. Plastics-user industries in Japan have already raised *per capita* consumption to the position of second in the world in a number of sectors.

It is this kind of consideration that has led to the astonishing growth of the plastics industry based on petrochemicals. In 1950 plastics represented only 4% of the total production of the Japanese chemical industry, but by 1960 the figure was 14% and rising steadily. As already mentioned, PVC production is one of the most outstanding features of the industry and completely dwarfs the production of polyethylene which itself is no mean performer at around 200,000 tons in 1965. However, the demand for polystyrene is below the 100,000 ton mark whilst copolymers like ABS are even less at around 20,000 tons. Polypropylene is made under licence from Montecatini and current demand is in the region of 30,000 tons a year. Oddly enough there is talk of giving up polypropylene altogether. Most of the other types of plastics are made including methacrylates, nylons, and fluorocarbons like PTFE. But Celluloid which started in 1909 in Japan, is still going strong. In the field of thermosetting resins too, Japan is a leading producer particularly in urea-formaldehyde. The reason is, of course, the very cheap urea available from Toyo Koatsu. Even in 1962 production was pushing the 200,000 ton mark.

Emphasis in plastics development is however not on the invention of chemically new plastics, but on what might be called the 'metallurgy' of plastics, that is to say on the improvement of properties by physical techniques or by minor chemical treatments. The ICI technique of crimping polyester fibres in 'Crimplene' is one example of the former. In fact many of the materials that scientists wish existed, would have properties which might be very difficult to achieve at the molecular level. In many ways the problem of finding a substitute for leather is just such a challenge, and one which has exercised the talents of some of the biggest and best chemical companies in the world. Du Pont in the United States have produced 'Corfam' and, rather late in the day, ICI are beginning the production of their version called 'Ortix' in the UK. In Japan several companies have tackled the problem, and it is interesting to look at one of the most notable of them to see just how good Japanese chemists can be in the business of originating new materials, as opposed to improving imported production know-how.

Japanese enterprise got its impulse from the fact that the country has to import 95% of its hides. Like most other Asian countries Japan has very little in the way of a dairy or beef industry so domestic hide production is very low. But the

Japanese like most other people have found that leather is far superior to other materials for shoe uppers. Most of the other possible materials like PVC have been tried and found wanting. And like scientists in other countries, Japanese workers have found that there is more to leather than meets the eye. It is not just that it is tough, flexible, more or less waterproof, yet still capable of breathing. It has curious mechanical properties as well. It stretches more in one direction than another, so that shoes expand sideways but not lengthways, it is capable of deforming permanently to accommodate irregularities of the feet like upstanding joints or bunions and it can also have the property of 'set retention', staying in the shape it had on the shoemaker's last. It can withstand a million flexes or more and it also looks nice in a way particularly difficult to imitate.

Making an artificial version of this was a tall order, but from 1960 onwards a number of Japanese companies began work. They included Kurashiki Rayon, Toyo Rubber, Hi-Telac and Nippon Cloth. Most of these were not strictly pure chemical companies but more plastics users and man-made fibre companies. Kurashiki Rayon's 'Clarino' has had a good deal of success and although manufacturing details are secret, it appears to be made along similar lines to 'Corfam' and 'Ortix'. The basic idea is to chop up nylon fibres and get them to take up a semi-random orientation in a basic mat or felt. These fibres have to stick to each other so the usual practice is to make them tacky for a while with a little solvent or stick them with a separate adhesive. In 'Clarino' some of the nylon fibres are crimped. In this way the material is easily deformed but only until the crimp or curl has been extended. It then displays the elasticity of straight nylon. The basal mat is needled to make sure it is microporous; it is then covered with a polyurethane topping. The next problem comes in making the pores in the topping. They have to be capable of resisting the passage of water in the liquid phase coming from outside but be able to transmit water in the vapour phase from inside. Techniques for doing this vary widely and are of critical importance. Some of the Japanese synthetic leathers, like Du Pont's 'Corfam', have a third layer between mat and the topping called an interlining. 'Eikas' by Nippon Cloth and 'Hi-Telac' have the often troublesome interlinings but Toyo Rubber's 'Patra' and 'Clarino' manage to do without.

So far as market response goes 'Clarino' and 'Hi-Telac' seem to be, if anything, more popular than 'Corfam' though price-cutting may alter this situation. Du Pont says that more was spent on developing 'Corfam' than on developing nylon itself, so for firms like Kurashiki Rayon to be in the same league is a very good performance indeed. Production in Japan is already running at up to 200,000 square metres per month, which is enough for 2.2 million pairs of shoes. As volume goes up, prices will fall and they are already low enough, at 70 pence per square foot, to compete with natural leather. 'Clarino' is not only good to look at, scuff-resistant, and instantly cleaned but is an 'engineering material'. In the shoe trade the implication of this is that automated machinery will at last be able to get into its stride, because before synthetic leathers came along only a skilled man could cope with the unpredictable vagaries of natural leather.

The ironic postcript to this fine performance of Japanese chemists is that an entrepreneur in Hong Kong is doing unto Japan what Japan traditionally did unto others. 'Look at this,' said one scandalised gentleman in a well-known Japanese trading company pulling out a pair of shoes. On the insoles was stamped the word 'Clarino'. Close examination showed that the material, which did closely resemble the new poromeric, was solid plastic with a fibrous flock sprayed on the back. 'This is the most blatant copying from some cheapjack in Hong Kong! Really this should not be allowed!'

The wheel of fortune has indeed moved a full circle.

TWELVE

Japan's Space Policy

But for what the Americans delicately call a malfunction involving a few explosive bolts it would have been possible to
write of Japan's space industry as a superb satellite-on-a-
shoestring performance. The hero would have been Japan's
own von Braun and the story could have been rounded off with
a scathing comparison of the British efforts which would have
cost so much more and achieved so much less. But a few explosive bolts went wrong, Japan's intended satellite plunged back
into the atmosphere and, since this was not the first failure, the
resulting political storm flung Japan's rocket father figure from
his position and, worse still, caused Japan to lose face among the
family of nations.

Up to 1966, and on a budget of less than £5 million a year,
the Tokyo scientists had made a serious attempt to be fourth
into space with their rocket, the Lambda 4S. By comparison a
nation like Britain had spent £35 million a year for nearly a decade and had not even tried to launch anything into orbit. On
24 September 1966, the Japanese Lambda 4S narrowly failed
to put a small satellite into orbit and since anyway it was a year
ahead of schedule the initial disappointment was easily forgiven
and the country's prestige remained high. Her policy was a
model of disciplined economy.

First of all Japan had decided what she wanted to do and set
about doing it with a singleness of purpose that British scientists
must have found enviable. Prime Minister Sato expressed himself thus: 'Since 1955 we in Japan, as participants in the world

programme of space exploration have been engaged in a series of space research programmes such as the observation of space by sounding rockets and I am looking forward to the further development of both space research and its application.' The test gantries at Spadeadam would have swayed with surprise if such words had come from Downing Street. Japan's space policy was forthright and assertive; 'space research, by shedding light on the actualities of outer space, serves as a valuable aid to the advancement of knowledge. Utilization of outer space for peaceful purposes has shown marked progress recently and it has become clear that further outstanding advances will be made. It is necessary that we pay special attention to the fact that the practical aspects, in particular, are being emphasized such as the utilization of rockets and satellites for meteorological observations, communications, navigation, goedetic survey, etc. Accordingly, we must vigorously push our programme along these lines. Space research contributes greatly to the prestige of science technology as well as to the development of new techniques.'

Even more surprising, Japan had not just one space programme but two and each of them planned to go into orbit with its own rocket. The two programmes originated in the University of Tokyo's Institute of Space and Aeronautical Science, and in the Government's Science and Technology Agency. The former has two test facilities at Noshiro and Kagoshima and the latter uses the Defence Agency's test centre at Niijima with another new centre at Tanegashima not far from Kagoshima. Although the expressed objectives of the two programmes each sounded as ambitious as the other, the University of Tokyo was far out ahead. They both got money from the Government but by different routes; Tokyo University is financed through the Ministry of Education, but the Science and Technology Agency is directly dependent on the Prime Minister's office.

In Japan, Tokyo University is like Oxford, Cambridge and Eton rolled into one. Its alumni are to be found in all the best jobs in the civil service and in the Government and, indeed, in the universities. It was where Professor Hideo Itogawa held a top job, and it was this man who would have become the von Braun of Japan. Unlike the latter, who was designing rockets during World War II, Itogawa was designing aircraft with Fuji Heavy Industries and his name was linked with an aircraft called the Hayabusha, second in fame to the Zero. It was Itogawa's enthusiasm that got things going as long ago as 1954. Japan started with solid fuels and first principles. The first rocket was less than an inch in diameter and known as Pencil. The second rocket weighed only two pounds and was hardly heavy enough to justify its name, Baby. In order to take part in the International Geophysical Year Japan developed the Kappa series and one of these rockets made a high sounding of 37 miles.

About this time the curious relationship with Japanese industry seems to have begun. Japanese companies showed avuncular kindness when it came to presenting the bills. Prince Motors developed solid propellants and Nippon Oils and Fats and Teikoku Manufacturing Company lent a hand. Japanese industry, represented by a special Space Committee of the Federation of Economic Organizations, provides most of the hardware and very little is imported. Mitsubishi's Kobe Shipyard, for example, produces pressure tanks and combustion chambers, and Prince Motors, now amalgamated with Nissan, have become outstanding in the field of solid propellants. Tokyo University's latest rocket, the MU series, develops 220,000 lb. thrust which is over half the size of the American space workhorse the 'Atlas' or the British 'Blue Streak'.

'Space on a shoe string' depended not only on the generosity of Japanese industry but on the choice of solid-fuelled rockets. It is possible to use numbers of old light-weight sounding rockets as strap-on boosters for bigger rockets and, except for Pencil and Baby, every rocket that Tokyo University has produced still sees service in some role or other with the latest space shots. The Lambda rockets, which made the first orbital attempts on 24 September 1966, form the upper stages of the new MU rocket and even the old Kappa sounding rockets are paired up and strapped on as boosters.

The MU rocket has a diameter of 54 inches which provides a considerable fuel-burning area. The Americans have tested rockets up to 200 inches in diameter but by current solid fuel standards the MU is quite a powerful machine. It should be able to orbit an 80 lb. satellite at between 100 and 1,000 miles high. The target date for this was early 1968.

The Science and Technology Agency also had plans to orbit a satellite by 1968. Their offshoot, the National Space Development Centre, having made some of its own rockets, hoped to use an advanced MU rocket with a liquid-fuelled third stage of its own design. This was an interesting departure, for solid fuels have their limitations. The main problem is that they cannot easily be switched on and off; it really amounts to a sophisticated version of lighting the blue touch paper and retiring. Other limitations are that the initial acceleration is very high, and with wide and therefore powerful rockets, the propellant can distort, sag, and even explode. The liquid-fuelled sustainer stage will be powered by unsymmetrical dimethyl hydrazine and kerosene. By the early 1970s pay loads of 350 lb. should have been placed in orbits at 620 miles.

So far there has been an air of improvisation about Japan's space programmes. There is, for example, no Press Office, and when the Lambda 4S was first launched at Kagoshima the Japanese pressmen, who are very competitive, stormed the gates. The position of Kagoshima, on the southern tip of Japan, makes it possible for rockets to be launched on slanting trajectories out over the Pacific; but although Kagoshima handles a launching frequency similar to that at Woomera, it has a permanent staff of only half a dozen people. When a launch is due about a hundred scientists descend on it from Tokyo, take off the dust covers and start things going. It therefore costs very little to run.

This was all very admirable and had Japan actually succeeded in putting a satellite into orbit on a total expenditure of $38 million (since 1960), there would have been loud applause round the world, and some hard questions in other space centres from Cape Kennedy to Les Landes and Woomera.

The first failure was of relative unimportance since Tokyo University had predicted only a 20 per cent chance of success. The solid-fuelled rocket, the Lambda 4S, had already proved to be a reliable sounding rocket in a three-staged configuration. This three-stager, code-named L-3H, had achieved a height of 1,120 miles earlier in 1966. The third stage nose-cone was replaced by a spherical motor (a sphere packed with propellant) with a cone-shaped satellite. The first failure of the new four-stage rocket was due to a third-stage deviation which occurred immediately after its separation. The correct sequence should have been for the third stage to be flipped over by small gas jets to a horizontal position, at which point the fourth stage should have separated and ignited, thus accelerating the 57 lb. satellite up to orbital velocity. However, the first attempt failed and the rocket fell back into the atmosphere after being tracked from as far away as Hawaii for nearly 20 minutes. The Tokyo University men were not down-hearted and prepared another shot for 20 December 1966.

Unfortunately this second attempt failed from causes apparently similar to those which provoked the first failure. This time a storm broke in the press for reasons which probably had as much to do with Tokyo University's handling of reporters as anything else. At first the attack focused on the one thing which, with better luck, might have earned Japan the highest praise: the shoestring budget.

Professor Hideo Itogawa held an explanatory press conference and admitted, 'We are professionals where sounding rockets are concerned, but amateurs when it comes to artificial satellites. But,' he declared, 'we will orbit one in 1968 at all costs.'

The press campaign against Tokyo University's Institute for Space and Aeronautical Science continued. The staff were accused of gross mismanagement of the Institute's affairs including some apparent financial irregularities. There were accusations about the 'Black Mist', referring to a special kind of constructive corruption which lubricates a good deal of Japanese industrial activity. It usually works by getting individual firms to be generous to politicians who may then be expected to be equally generous in recommending some project for government support. When the project is funded, the firms in question get the contracts. The only people the money usually sticks to are the real politicans – but when a scandal starts the mud flies in all directions. The Socialist Party then dug up an old controversy about the export of rockets to Indonesia in 1965. Professor Itogawa, who had driven the Institute into the van of rocket progress, was naturally at the centre of the row. He is an intense, vigorous man with a good command of English and a very clear and ordered mind. His vision had been that the Tokyo University Institute should launch scientific satellites with its own simple rockets, and motives such as national pride seem to have played little part in his determination to put up a Japanese satellite. Under the heavy barrage of complaint which came from unfavoured industrialists as much as from self-righteous journalists, he decided to resign. He left on 20 March. On 13 April a third Lambda 4S launching went wrong and the Institute of Space and Aeronautical Science came under even heavier attack. In 1967 very little went right for anybody concerned with Japan's space effort. The next scapegoat was an electronics expert, Professor Takagi, a genial friendly man, who had been appointed to co-ordinate Tokyo University's work with that of the rival camp, the Space and Technology Agency (STA). He was Director of the National Space Development Centre financed by the STA and also head of the University's Space Programmes. He offered his resignation on 30 June on the grounds of ill health.

A note of high farce crept into these unsavoury proceedings when the fishermen of Kagoshima would not allow the STA space centre scientists at Tanegashima to light the blue touch paper under their smaller weather research rockets. Later, these same fishermen blocked activities at the University of Tokyo's centre in the same area. At both these centres of advanced technology, the scientists switched off their computers and went home to await the end of the fishing season in late August. Naturally this meant losing even more face but at least the discomfort was shared between Tokyo University and the STA.

Meanwhile, Professor Takagi was prevailed upon to remain at his post for some time longer. When he was called to the Diet to explain the Lambda 4S failure, he became the target for attack by two other professors, Professor Tetsuchi Okamoto of Tokyo University's Engineering Department and Professor Ichiro Shirag of Meiji University. They claimed that the Institute's explanatory reports were insufficient since nearly 90 per cent of the contents were just test plans. There were heavily sarcastic remarks about the secrecy of the Institute, and a socialist politician, Yoshio Miki, said that the reports contained lies. Asking the unfortunate Takagi why the fourth stage of the last Lambda 4S had 'dropped off' (the explosive separation bolts had presumably failed again) he remarked that clearly Takagi was not qualified to work on such a project.

By the beginning of 1968 it seemed as if the shoestring days were over when the STA revealed the N rocket proposal. This project was reputed to cost $416 million over five years, thereby dwarfing the $38 million or so already spent by Tokyo University. If successful, the STA would leapfrog the Tokyo University work because the N rocket, with an initial thrust of 660,000 lbs. would be able to put 330 lbs. into the geostationary 22,000 mile orbit occupied by Early Bird and Intelsat communication satellites. This would be far in excess of the performance of the MU rockets and comparable with the best that the European ELDO PAS rockets were supposed to achieve. Unfortunately the STA can hardly be said to be building on experience since their biggest rockets so far are the LS-C sounding rockets with a thrust of only 37,400 lbs.

However, this proposal does have the merit of conforming with government policy which broadly speaking sees the STA as producing the launchers and Tokyo University as producing the scientific exploration satellites. The other trump card the STA have in hand is the fact that their proposals have the backing of the aerospace firms which will carry out the research on behalf of the Agency. By contrast Tokyo University has kept research strictly within the confines of the institute, leaving manufacturers to do no more than turn out the hardware.

There is no doubt but that the N rocket programme if successful would make Japan into a formidable rocket power with a greatly enhanced bargaining position in the International Telecommunications Satellite Consortium (Intelsat). The Tokyo University Institute has produced some powerful arguments against the development, and the controversy continues. One point made is that such a risky and expensive venture is unnecessary when Japan can use American rockets to launch its satellites. This is true but there are strings attached, notably the need to subscribe to the single global satellite communications system. Another argument is that the N rocket could well be obsolete before it is fired, but that is an argument against going into any technologically advanced project in which the Americans are competing. A stronger argument is that Japan must walk before she runs, and learn to succeed with little Lambdas before raising the price of failure by using bigger rockets.

It must not be thought from this account that space studies are the preoccupation exclusively of these two rival camps. Many other organisations are involved in studies which are directly related to the demands of satellite technology. The Ministry of Transport's Ship Research Institute has been studying navigational satellite requirements since 1965. The Hydrographic Office, experimenting with satellite geodesy, has just moved an island 600 km. south of Tokyo about one mile to the west on its charts. Research institutes belonging to MITI are involved in everything from the new wonder material carbon fibre to vacuum techniques for space environmental facilities. The Ministry of Posts and Telecommunications has a serious project afoot to launch a Japanese-made communications satellite into a geostationary orbit by 1973. This will depend on the N rocket programme for launching but the United States has offered to help Japan by providing detailed technical information on other thorny problems like satellite attitude control systems. Apart from this, the Americans have also expressed a willingness to launch Japanese satellites for them.

Japanese industry also likes to boast of its participation in space activities. Whatever the single-minded scientists of Tokyo think about space, industrialists certainly think it glamorous; it enables them to print the sort of advertisements the American aerospace companies love: a background shot of a distant galaxy with words like ' . . . a hostile environment . . . Our equipment has proved itself', etc. In the foreground there is usually a mass of electronics and the company's name. Because it looks good and the government money feels good, who can resist it?

Even when Japan was not as rich as she is now, Professor Itogawa managed to get the financial support he needed. During the '64 recession, there was no diminution in the flow of funds for the space programme and although the sums were small the total drain on resources should not be minimised. One of the explanations provided by the British for the low cost certainly has something to be said for it. The famous $38 million did not include the salaries of university scientists nor the cost of university services, and overheads are as high in rocketry as anywhere else in industry. Perhaps a better figure for a typical year's expenditure, quoted as £4$\frac{1}{2}$ million (old exchange rate) in 1965, might have been around £12 million. Nevertheless Japan has clearly had much more for her money than Britain which has regularly spent £35 million since 1960.

One important difference between the Japanese and British space programmes is the use of solid-fuelled rockets rather than the more complex liquid-fuels system used in Blue Streak. As already mentioned, solid rockets do suffer from some disadvantages in that initial acceleration tends to be high and equipment tends to get a bigger battering than with liquid fuels. The other problem is that solid fuel could not be switched off or used for second burns. This provision for controllability need not be built into the lowest booster, however, and in the STA plans it will be the small third stage which will have a liquid-fuel system. To this extent Japanese rockets seem to have the virtue of inbuilt economy.

There is one other factor in the Japanese scene which ought to be discussed and perhaps it accounts for much of the sureness with which space objectives are being pursued. As Professor

Takagi puts it, space is Japan's only 'big science'. This phrase 'big science', is applied to certain projects in which scientific research is directly integrated with advanced technological activity on a large scale. The atomic energy industry is one example, advanced aviation is another, fundamental particle research with large accelerators is yet another and oceanography is moving quickly into this scope of definition.

For the Japanese, aviation and nuclear physics were out of the question after the war. One of the first things General MacArthur did on landing was to ship Japan's two cyclotrons and associated equipment, tow them into the Pacific and sink them. The aviation industry was so effectively dispersed that it has taken twenty years to recover. Space research is different – it is not, or at least it was not, in any way commercial. Under the wing of Tokyo University, it was purely scientific and educational. Yet it was advanced and challenging. Today, it sets competition targets for electronics, metallurgy, engine designers, control gear manufacturers; it lets the Japanese rub shoulders with Americans at Cape Kennedy, with the British at Farnborough; it is spectacular and internationally significant. It also does a great deal for Japan's image in the eyes of its own scientific élite. Japan, too, has a brain drain which flows merrily, in spite of the best possible restraint being provided by the Japanese language and script. Many young scientists learn English, go to work in America and come back with great reluctance only when family pressures are exerted. Putting satellites into orbit means that Japan stops looking provincial in their eyes. It may not be a world force but at least it is trying to put up satellites and that activity confers distinction.

Inside Japan, opposition to space activity comes from the Socialists. At a recent sitting of the Diet budgetary committee, a Socialist Party member put the ritual question, 'Will Japan's space development later be changed for military purposes?' The answer is 'No,' partly because the Japanese say so, but also because, without nuclear warheads, rockets are prohibitively expensive ways of delivering destructive force. Satellites do have some significance for Japanese defence, however, in the shape of spy satellites. However much Japan trusts the United States to defend her, she does not trust the Americans to do her spying. If surveillance satellites can tell the Japanese Government what China or Russia are up to, then at least they can start prodding their protectors.

When the top men in Japan's space activities are asked to list the reasons for their space programmes they put technological spin-off first and admit that it may be as much psychological as practical; they emphasise the stimulus it gives to industries which co-operate and they point out that they will be in a good position to co-operate as a nation in the space industry of the future. They usually put national prestige last, and this does not seem to be merely for the benefit of the foreign visitor. The lack of publicity services and the extreme difficulty which foreign journalists are likely to encounter when they want to tell the story of Japan in space seem to support this view. The Japanese Government, however, clearly appreciates the effect space club membership will have on the reputation of exported manufactures.

THIRTEEN

Computers: Japanese or American?

In no other field are the penalties of not doing enough of your own research being made so clear as in computers. The problems of the industry, it used to be said, were a three-letter word, IBM. Recently, however, a two-letter word has come into view: IC. Between them International Business Machines (IBM) and Integrated Circuits (IC), as patented mainly by Texas Instruments, have got Japan into an awkward corner and it's fascinating to see what the Japanese are doing about it.

Once the world of business is converted to the view that computers are necessary and begins to see that scientific management in particular requires large computers, the American domination of the whole field rapidly becomes unacceptable. At the British Ministry of Technology, the reaction was vigorous, if belated. They believed that if Britain did not maintain her own computer industry she would 'lose her industrial birthright'. The native computer industry was transfused with money and managerial talent and began slowly to fight back. In France, Machines Bull could not repeat the trick. Dependence on America was demonstrated in no uncertain fashion when the United States Government banned the export of the largest IBM 360 to France, because it was needed to facilitate the manufacture of hydrogen bombs. IBM has over 95 per cent of the world market and its amazing success has brought it more problems than it could ever have imagined possible. Its competitors, wherever they are, find themselves protected and helped in every possible way; Japan is no different.

In Japan 40 per cent of the computers by number and 60

per cent by value are made by IBM. The Japanese market is the second largest in the world after the United States. At the end of March, 1965, there were 24,500 computers in operation in the United States, 1,840 in Japan with West Germany, France and Britain following at about the 1,300 mark. With the Japanese economy back on a nine per cent growth rate, with aggressive technologically-minded managements and with no company so old that the chairman can say, 'we've done very well in the past without them', Japan represents a golden market for computers. It is little wonder that IBM is doing everything in its power to stay *persona grata*.

IBM has been manufacturing computers in Japan since 1963 and trying to look like a Japanese company as much as possible. All the directors on the board are Japanese nationals with only one exception, a solitary American. The rest of the company is solidly Japanese. It is, however, wholly owned by IBM in the United States, which could, if it chose, fire the whole board and close down the company. Since all the profits have been ploughed back to finance expansion for many years past, this is unlikely to happen. Repatriating profits to the United States has proved difficult for some American companies, but as Japan moves towards freer trade policies these 'difficulties' should ease, so that by the time IBM expects to see a return on its investment, repatriating should be no problem.

The dominance of American technology in the computer field is not confined to IBM. Univac has about sixteen per cent of the Japanese home market while National Cash Register has another three per cent. Japanese-built computers account for about thirty-eight per cent of the market, but many of these are American computers made under licence. There are now six domestic producers; Hitachi which has an agreement with RCA, Nippon Electric linked with Honeywell, Toshiba with General Electric, Oki with Univac, and Mitsubishi Electric with Bunker Ramo. Two of these, Oki and Mitsubishi are joint venture companies. The sixth is Fujitsu, one of the biggest manufacturers: it has not got an agreement with anyone; its computers are designed and made entirely in Japan.

Most of these companies are like English Electric was in Britain. That is to say they are heavily involved in other activities which make a firm base for operations and none of them is likely to stand or fall like ICL on the basis of its computer manufacturing ability alone. Fujitsu and NEC, for example, specialise in telecommunications, whilst Hitachi spreads its net so wide that it accounts for two per cent of Japan's gross national product. There is also, in Japan, a proud history of computer research which gives considerable confidence to the domestic industry.

Relay computers were made over fifteen years ago for camera manufacturers daunted by the complexity of lens calculations, and ten years ago a 'Parametron' computer was invented at Tokyo University. Fifty of these unique computers were sold but they were too slow and too expensive, incorporating as they did, rather large ferrite cores and capacitors. A number of computers with valves were also manufactured and with the coming of the germanium transistor in 1959 Fujitsu designed the Facom 222 which counted in decimals and had a store of ten thousand words. For the manufacturers however it was an uphill task. For example most of the banks doubted the reliability of Japanese computers and thought it better to stick to IBM. Use by a bank appears to be an accolade of merit in Japan, and Fujitsu regards the purchase of one of its computers by the Dai-ichi Bank as a milestone for the Japanese computer industry as a whole.

The Japanese Government recognised early on the importance of computers and as long ago as 1957 passed the Electronic Industry Promotion Provisional Act. The electronics industry was recognised as a 'strategic' industry. The manufacturers of computers then established the Japan Electronic Industry Development Association which is not to be compared with a British style co-operative Research Association. It does not do what the industry thinks there would be no harm in doing as tends to happen in Britain. It concerns itself with matters of vital commercial significance; for example it is presently engaged in developing, with government help, a giant computer comparable to IBM's 360-90 or the CDC 6600. Another body of much greater importance in sustaining the health of the Japanese computer industry is JECC, the Japanese Electronic Computer Company.

JECC has a paid up capital of 8.8 million pounds invested by the six domestic manufacturers but in recent years its operating budget was 30 million pounds. JECC pays computer manufacturers for computers which it then leases to customers. That is to say, if a manufacturer disposes of a computer to a customer, as result of normal sales activity, the customer may ask JECC if he can rent it. If JECC approves, the manufacturer gets the money, the customer gets the computer whilst JECC gets the rent and title. Now eighty per cent of all computers are rented in Japan so JECC's involvement is very important. A committee judges the suitability of a new computer for leasing and is currently squeezing out American material. Naturally a wholly IBM or Univac computer is ineligible, but a Japanese-built computer with too much American material in it is also likely to be turned down. In JECC's first year of existence, the minimum amount of Japanese material which could qualify for support was twenty per cent, in the second year fifty per cent and so on. The order of merit is first, a pure Japanese computer like Fujitsu's, second, a Japanese computer made under licence but with Japanese components, and third a joint venture.

Where does the money come from? Some comes directly from the Government, some comes from the Japan Development Bank (Government-backed) and some comes from other banks. In the end it boils down to a very subtle and complex instrument bringing carefully graduated but unrelenting support to the home industry. It goes without saying that individual manufacturers can all get cheap loans for computer expansion from the Government. They also get special depreciation allowances.

What about the Japanese company with the 'highest posture', the company which has no imported technology, but which still manages to sell as much as Hitachi and NEC and has ten per cent of the market, the Fujitsu company? The source of Fujitsu's strength is the communications business and in this the company can claim to be up at the front. Its laboratories have developed electronic telephone exchanges and pulsed code modulation systems which are now on sale. It is also developing thin film integrated circuits and has now begun the mass-production of integrated silicon chips which are destined for its new series of computers. The Facom 230 range is subdivided from small to large, from 10 to 80 on the style of IBM's 360 series. At present only the medium 230 40 and the largest 230 60 will have integrated circuits, but the whole future of integrated circuits (ICs) is causing Japan a big headache. More about this later.

Fujitsu now ranks with Hitachi and NEC as one of the largest domestic suppliers but the future will be different. Hanzo Omi, the executive director, likes to draw a graph of sales. One line shows the steady growth of other domestic producers who are prevented by their licence agreements from exporting. The other line, after a slow take-off, goes shooting up overtaking all competitors. That, he says, is Fujitsu with all the world for a market. Fujitsu has made a good start by selling sixty computers to Bulgaria, two to the Philippines and one to South Korea. The picture is not however quite as simple as that. Japanese manufacturers with technical agreements are not going to let the situation continue. Hitachi for example, has sold one computer to the Trans-Siberian Railway for seat reservations. In any case in other industries the pattern has been to manufacture under licence first in order to learn, and then to launch out alone. This tactic works well under protection and Japanese computers are going to be protected for a long time to come by means too subtle for GATT.

Fujitsu has much to be proud of. It has not only designed and manufactured a range of computers which can provide credible alternatives to other major computer ranges like those of IBM, RCA or ICL, but it has also embarked on the manufacture of peripheral equipment. Such equipment when bought from American competitors, the Japanese say, often suffers inexplicable delivery delays so Fujitsu has decided on complete independence. About half their staff is devoted to software development and this is now the only field in which Japanese universities play a part, The software has not developed the sales subtleties of IBM or ICT as yet; there is, for example, no technique of mimicking a competitor's computer, so that the customer may be encouraged to relinquish an old loyalty by the knowledge that he need not throw away his old software as well.

Software specialisation began in October 1966 with the setting up of Japan Soft Ware Co. Ltd., by Hitachi, NEC, and Fujitsu. It will undertake development of software and consultant services for domestic electronic computers.

The Japanese Government clearly finds IBM a thorn in its side but the advent of integrated circuits seems likely to produce another one, potentially just as big, in the shape of Texas Instruments.

The differences between transistors and ICs or silicon planar technology are somewhat rarefied but in general it may be said that a transistor will have only one function, working like a valve, either stopping or letting through a signal depending on whether a voltage is or is not applied across it. Most existing computers depend on them. Integrated circuits are made by taking a piece of silicon and diffusing into it various impurities in a controlled way so as to alter its electrical properties. By connecting up various parts of such a crystal it is possible to make it behave as if it were a complete circuit of many transsistors, even including capacitors and resistances. Up to 270 transistors have been built into one chip of silicon as small as a clipping from a baby's finger nail. One of the virtues of ICs is that, having so little mass, they do themselves no damage if shocked or knocked about; for this reason the United States defence programmes have developed them to a high degree of perfection. It is no surprise to learn therefore that most of the patents that cover the most economical means of production are held by American companies like Fairchild and Texas Instruments Inc.

Japan has made its fortune by importing foreign know-how and foreign companies are getting increasingly tough over the royalties. The Japanese computer manufacturers may import integrated circuits, but if they wish to manufacture them under licence, not only must they accept restrictions on exporting them but, and this has been the latest shock, Japan must accept as part of the deal a wholly-owned subsidiary of Texas Instruments in Japan itself. This is not to the Government's liking and up to 1968 they would not budge beyond a fifty-fifty ownership. Texas Instruments was equally obdurate.

These matters have suddenly become more important because of desk calculators. In ordinary computers ICs are not yet of vital importance, although they will be present in many of the next computer generation. Desk calculators are really miniature computers and the Japanese regard ICs as indispensable for them because they will make the calculators smaller, lighter and above all cheaper. Electronic desk calculators have to compete with mechanical machines and in order to keep down the costs they need to be made in large quantities. Long production runs can only be justified if export prospects are good, but if they cannot be exported to the United States, what then? Various companies like Fujitsu are doing their best to make their own ICs and avoid infringing patents, and one can be sure that the Japanese government's own laboratories are hard at work as well.

Even so for the first time the expansion of a Japanese industry in overseas markets looks like being severely hampered by the fact that the know-how is imported. Desk calculators may not sound a very vital line of products but the growth in the last two years has been phenomenal. Hayakawa and Canon Camera were first in the field in 1964, but since then nine other companies have ventured into this new market. Total production at 1,700 sets in 1964 went to 25,000 the year after, and 60,000 in 1967. This will be worth about $27 million, and half the output is already being exported. Sony have produced a portable model, Toshiba a timesharing model, and one model from Hayakawa is less than one foot square and six inches deep and weighs only twelve pounds. The surge of fierce competition is already following a familiar pattern.

Integrated circuits have many other applications and are widely heralded as starting a new era in electronics development.

The first IC radios are ready and many applications in the television field will soon be marketed. What Japan did with the transistor is going to be repeated all over again with ICs, or so the industry confidently predicts. Already 53 million dollars has been spent on direct IC manufacturing investment excluding research and development (1968). Fujitsu is followed by most of the major names in Japanese electronics, Hitachi, Nippon Electric, Oki, Kyodo, Matsushita and about half a dozen more. Already there are complaints about heavy royalty payments to the United States.

The Japanese Government is being forcibly reminded by the computer industry and IC circuit makers that the days of good profits from foreign know-how are over. The answer in the future is likely to be more original research and less hard bargaining over imported expertise.

FOURTEEN

The Technology Gap

A Western businessman in Tokyo put it crudely but tersely. 'They've been rumbled at last. After twenty years of selling the Japs technological know-how, other countries are beginning to realise that they've been handing out rods for their own backs and it's going to stop.'

In this context 'other countries' means the United States, West Germany, Britain and Switzerland, with the first-named providing well over half the rods. The United States has also been the first to complain and the recent hardening in her attitude is one of the factors that has led the Japanese Government to examine with some urgency the technological gap between Japan and the West. American firms have been raising their royalty rates, the Radio Corporation of America is reported to be squeezing Hitachi for six per cent of sales revenue for some know-how and the rate is generally around four per cent. Some foreign companies are simply refusing to sell, especially now that Japan is a dangerous competitor in world markets. In exchange for know-how, American companies are demanding to be allowed to form joint venture companies or to establish wholly-owned subsidiaries. Indeed, at the time of writing, Texas Instruments which owns much of the integrated circuit know-how is severely hampering the latest desk calculator boom by insisting on permission to establish a wholly-owned subsidiary in Japan before releasing licences. American General Electric recently increased its holding of Tokyo Shibaura Electric shares in exchange for know-how. Another severe restriction more and more often imposed is that of limiting the area to which products may be exported. In 1967 about two thirds of technical know-how contracts included these clauses.

It can be seen therefore that, as a direct consequence of the technological gap, Japan is being forced to open her doors to foreign capital in a manner which is not of her choosing and she is being obliged to limit her export markets. It is not surprising therefore that MITI has taken alarm and is increasing Government aid for research and development. In fact the whole field of science policy is in for a considerable reappraisal.

Up to five or six years ago the spectacle of Japan's economic growth coupled with her remarkably low expenditure on research and development made many economists wonder if 'R and D' was worth doing except in the military sphere. In communications, electronics and chemicals it was calculated that up to sixty per cent of Japan's sales were due to the exploitation of foreign 'R and D', and with firms in other industries the proportion might be up to a quarter. It seemed that, provided some other country was generous enough to take the original risks, it made more commercial sense to buy a licence and concentrate on squeezing the best out of it. From the mid-fifties onwards licensing in Japan showed a very steep increase. In 1956 there were 311 cases calling for a payout of 33 million dollars, but by 1962 the number of new contracts had gone up to 757 entailing payments of over 114 million dollars. The scale of the activity was so great that it had to be regulated by statute. The Foreign Investment Law requires that any contracts running for longer than one year and costing more than 30,000 dollars must be authorised by MITI after individual screening. The Japanese freely admit that most of their rapid technical progress has depended on imported technology and by 1966 194 million dollars a year was paid out in foreign exchange. Against this Japan earned only 15.7 million dollars from the export of her own technology. The ratio of receipts to payments was only 7 to 93 whereas in West Germany the ratio is 30 to 70. The ratio for the United States is 91 to 9, receipts/payments. Since the early fifties Japan has paid out a grand total of around

1,000 million dollars for foreign know-how and it has been a wonderful bargain.

The extraordinary thing about this vital importation of expertise is that Japan has been reluctant and grudging in paying for it. Firms licensing Japanese companies often come out of the experience wondering who's doing the favour. Particularly unfortunate are the European and American agencies who handle the transactions in Japan. The usual form is for the donor and recipient companies to achieve a hard-fought bargain after long negotiations made particularly frustrating by the Japanese inability to say 'yes' or 'no' in so many words. Eventually the agreement is ready but first has to be screened by MITI. At this point the trouble may only just be starting because MITI will not only delay matters without explanation but will invariably further modify the agreement in favour of the Japanese firm. MITI is particularly hostile to no-export agreements and to minimum royalty payments. The latter are agreements whereby the licensee agrees to pay a minimum fee whether the percentage on the sales reaches the figure or not. MITI is also careful to make sure that agreements are not devised so that Japanese companies can sit on a new technological development and stop other firms from operating it.

An apologia for the sort of behaviour that has reduced several honest negotiators to ulcers goes as follows: 'It's true that recent licensing agreements approved by MITI may look ungenerous: something like a three to four per cent royalty on an agreement to run no longer than five years, with renewal after that often being dependent on the terms being revised downward. But remember that a lot of these recent agreements have really been tail-end ones of the 'first gap' industrial revolution. At the beginning of the 1950s, the Americans, who at that time provided perhaps ninety per cent of the know-how agreements, exploited a monopoly position. When the Europeans entered in much greater numbers, the Japanese government felt entitled to signal to Japanese firms that prices could drop because the market in these 'old-style industrial revolution techniques' had become more competitive. But for really basic new technology of the emerging new scientific revolution, the Japanese government is beginning to get more prompt and a little more generous.'

They have a point, for some of the older kinds of know-how may not necessarily have cost very much to acquire. On the other hand the bargaining power of someone selling more recent know-how is that much more strong so the Japanese just have to be more generous. One new trend is to swap information. When Fuji Iron and Steel wanted the National Steel Corporation's know-how on galvanising they had to trade their own knowledge of chromium-plating to get it. Another technique is to sell MITI a special agreement for them to play with. Experienced operators can predict what will happen and, as likely as not, MITI's modifications will reduce the agreement to something very close to the one the two companies have already agreed on in secret.

Nevertheless the writing is on the wall and Japan will have to set about doing her own research and development in a much bigger way than at present.

One early initiative is worth looking at in some detail and ironically it is itself an imported idea. After taking a hard look at the British National Research and Development Corporation (NRDC) Japan decided to set up an analogous body called JRDC. An account of JRDC may give the impression that it is the most important of the Government's initiatives but of course this is not so. It is simply one of the easiest to locate and describe and it is general in its application whereas some other measures like civil development contracts are quite narrow and specific. Looking at JRDC also sheds an interesting ray of light on the Japanese approach to innovation.

JRDC operates in a rather freer way than NRDC and so far the total investment is much smaller. In 1966 its capital was less than £2 million of Government money, on which no interest is paid. The Corporation was established in 1961 by a Government Act and so far it is little known even within the civil service. One reason is that, unlike NRDC it has not had the good fortune to back a spectacular invention like the hovercraft. Nor is it seen as a corrective to that curious habit the British have of making brilliant inventions and then buying back the developed version, at great expense, from the Americans.

In Japan the private inventor seems to be rare and JRDC is much more concerned with developing the fruits of research in universities and Government laboratories. This, of course, is NRDC's main activity too. Unlike NRDC, however, JRDC would never give a researcher money and would not find itself setting up anything like Hovercraft Development Ltd. or the Dracone subsidiary. On the other hand, it does not demand the transfer of patents to itself as does NRDC: the researcher keeps the patents in his own name.

JRDC has a permanent staff of about fifty people, mainly scientists, who receive about eighty projects a year. Usually around ten will be taken up after approval by a development council. This council consists of nine men drawn equally from industry and university circles with one or two financiers. The current finance man is from the Government's Japan Development Bank. The council can co-opt specialists for the occasion, but has ultimately to make up its own mind and arrive at, preferably unanimous, decisions. In doubtful cases it can resort to voting.

When a piece of research has been selected for development, details are announced in newspapers and in an official bulletin. Firms who are interested and wish to take up development then apply to JRDC which selects the best of them. At this point observers of the British industrial scene will note significant differences between the experience of JRDC and its British counterpart. Out of forty-four projects backed by JRDC, only one failed to take off because of lack of enthusiasm on the part of industrialists. This is one reason why JRDC has not, so far, had to set up joint development companies. The state of the Japanese economy is closer to Adam Smith's model than some others and there is no lack of enthusiasm in taking up a new idea if there is any prospect of commercial return. JRDC's policies directly encourage this because the chosen firm cannot easily lose.

JRDC makes a contract with the firm in question and provides a sum of money. If the firm is successful with the development it has to repay the loan within five years and pay a royalty. Half of this royalty goes to JRDC and half to the original inventor. If the development is only marginally successful repayment of the loan can be postponed so as to take, say, eight years. If, however, the development fails then JRDC says goodbye to its money and that is the end of it. In the initial contract the developing firm is given exclusive licensing rights for an agreed period provided the proper royalties are paid. The period of exclusive rights is usually three years.

A glance through the list of forty-odd projects so far supported gives an interesting insight into Japanese innovations. Most of the projects involve an improvement to existing processes and there is a marked absence of the far-out radical ideas with which NRDC often finds itself embroiled. There are no universal vegetable harvesters, or pivoting flexible ships; instead a series of solid, sensible and not too expensive innovations whose value is immediately meaningful to cautious industrialists. Some examples include a better method of making lithium aluminium hydride, better methods of baking quartz crystals to achieve stability, a better coal-gas converter burner (this one was abandoned), a new method of growing large quartz crystals, and a new method of making seamless plastic bags. Some of the reports have a familiar ring. A report on a new method of extracting magnesium oxide from serpentine, which has been carried through to completion, says, 'but the cost of the product was not so low as we had expected at first'. Nothing in the list will reach the moon but they all stand a good chance of making a profit.

JRDC's executive director, Hisashi Harada, says that one of the things Japan lacks is a private version of his own Government-financed organisation. He has in mind a Japanese version of the British Technical Development Capital Ltd (TDC) which is at present almost submerged in ICFC. He has declared that in his view private banks and even the Japan Development Bank are incapable of supporting innovation. It was not just that banks want guarantees but that their evaluation is not expert enough when it comes to judging the prospects for an innovation.

JRDC was one initiative but not only does it not go far enough but the philosophy implied by its existence is perhaps basically erroneous. That seems to be what the examiners of the OECD (Organisation for Economic Co-operation and Development) are saying when they remark that '... review of these measures to date suggests that there is not yet a clear appreciation that the fruits of fundamental research may be different in kind from investment in a technically improved product or process. Research should not primarily be conceived as a technical service to existing manufacturing operations, but as the arrow which shows the direction in which manufacturing can move.'

The OECD review of Japan's science policy has other strictures, pointing out that there is little in the way of research associations (though many would question their value), that research in Government laboratories is at a low level and ill co-ordinated, and that University research must be brought into the picture. Furthermore they don't like the way the two top advisory councils, the Science Council and the Council for Science and Technology, are at permanent loggerheads. Allocation of money for 'R and D' is also inflexible and needs to become more experimental and more venturesome. Indeed in the whole report the only thing which gets a favourable nod is the plan to make a Research Park at Mount Tsukuba by sending there many of the Government research laboratories. This is a most impressive development in which there will be 'several universities, some forty Government research institutions plus some private ones'. It will be connected to Tokyo by a thirty-mile expressway, and it will be ready in ten years' time. The Japanese hope that there will be a recapitulation of the experience the Americans had with the Massachussetts Institute of Technology and the inflorescence of science-based firms which has grown up around it and along the local expressway Route 128.

The point is of course that no country has a perfect blueprint for science research and development policy. The British spend a bigger proportion of the GNP on research than any other country except the United States and have precious little to show for it in terms of economic growth. In the United States, innovation comes in all shapes and sizes, some as spin-off from space and defence research, some from big rich firms like General Electric who run their own quasi-academic research centres, some from private inventors operating in an industrial environment that will always try something new. Nobody knows, for example, just how productive the big science band-wagons will be, space programmes, fast breeder reactors and so on. Gingerly Japan is joining in. To them space, for example, is not just a field of human endeavour; it will also be good business because of communications satellites. Atomic energy will also be good business because Japan has exhausted her profitable hydro-electric power and her coal industry is in decline.

Other straws in the wind include four civil development contracts from MITI. Announced in late 1967, these were for a jet engine in the 20,000-30,000 lb. thrust class which they characterise as 'medium size', for a sea-water distillation plant, for a high-efficiency battery and a new way round ICI's ammonia plant patents. These are not in themselves likely to make much difference to the parlous state of fundamental research but they will help to save future imports of foreign technology. If the successor to the YS 11 sells well, the Japanese don't want to pay out the profits to Rolls Royce so they need their own jet; for desalination Japan herself needs water from the sea, and as for the battery, the small electric town car will have to come in Japanese cities at least as soon as in Los Angeles or Paris.

When it comes to the figures, it may seem at first sight that Japan is not so badly off. In terms of the proportion of the GNP devoted to research, Japan ranks with West Germany at 1.4 per cent compared to the 2.3 per cent of Britain and 3.4 per cent of the United States. In terms of people employed she comes second in the world after the United States with about one quarter the number, 187,000 compared to 700,000. The proportion of the total expenditure which comes from the Government is very low, however, at 28 per cent. In a world league table drawn up on that basis, Japan comes nearly at the bottom. There are those critics of Government intervention who could see the latter figures as a healthy sign. To confuse further those about to draw hasty conclusions, it must be added that the Japanese themselves say that much of the 'R and D' effort goes into squeezing value out of existing technology rather than original work. The statisticians and head-counters have not yet burrowed sufficiently deep for the Government to get a clear picture of the situation, though they have published some graphs purporting to show the difference between production gain due to capital and labour changes and that due to 'advance of technologies'.

Total government support for research and development is going up. MITI's contribution in 1968 was to be raised from 2.8 million pounds to 10 million pounds (pre-devaluation rates) and the overall percentage of the GNP is to be raised to 2.5 per cent by 1971. Other measures in the pipeline are the raising of the tax exemption rate (from 25 to 30 per cent) on development projects and making tax free all the profit from the sale of know-how inside Japan. A Government-financed service centre will be set up to provide information on technology especially news from overseas; the patent system is also due for a brush-up. Another problem the Government promises to tackle is the lack of interchange between University people (who are officially civil servants) and industry, with the possibility of consultancy services growing up.

In general the Japanese Government is now very conscious of the technology gap and the usual spate of administrators' tips and winks has begun with many inspired articles saying remarkably little of substance but adding up to an important change in the business climate. The nagging doubt that remains is whether Japan can, in fact, turn up the winners.

Much of the technology that Japan does export like the Toyo Koatsu Urea process is technical optimisation and only a few things like the tunnel diode can be identified as really original inventions. True creativity may well be turned on like a tap but so far nobody knows. The existence of Nobel prizewinning physicists like Yukawa suggests that the Japanese mind, even if it doesn't express itself in a logical language, is well capable of sustained and profound insight. The important thing is the social climate, and here there is still too much conformity and insufficient tolerance for the eccentric. Since the Government has decreed that Japan must have home-made innovation, it is quite likely that even now a task group is collecting data on Frank Whittle, Christopher Cockerell and Bell Laboratories with a view to making the necessary adjustments. As a postscript it must be added that the world already owes to Japan an invention found in every household in all industrialised nations. As long ago as 1908 Dr Kikunae Ikeda of Tokyo University discovered monosodium glutamate, and this substance has been enhancing flavours for the world's food manufacturers ever since.

FIFTEEN

Imports: The Containment Policy

It is often said that in the process of economic expansion Japan has had a relatively easy time 'because she has been simply catching up with existing techniques in the West'. This view is so oversimplified as to be completely untrue. Other countries too, like India or Brazil, have 'simply had to catch up with the West' but they have had an agonising time trying to do so, and some of their biggest problems have been in the all-important field of the balance of payments. Japan likewise has faced the most daunting problems in this area and the way in which she has tackled them is an example to other nations. The United Kingdom in particular needs to ponder deeply on Japan's success and the reasons which lie behind it.

The first thing to note is that as a percentage of her national output Japan's exports are only ten per cent, whereas Britain manages to export sixteen per cent of her GNP. These figures are for 1965 so, even as Britain was swinging into the recession that led to the 1967 devaluation, she was exporting a greater volume than Japan and still heading into a balance of payments crisis. The important thing is not just to drive up exports, but to balance imports against them.

Japan has a long history of success in this balancing trick and one technique recently used dates back to the Sino-Japanese war. This was the 'link' system, and it had not only a special subtlety but an important educational value as well. In the early fifties when imports and exports were controlled Japanese firms were granted import licences for particular commodities only if they exported specified manufactured goods. It was a sort of mini-balance of payments situation for each firm which wanted to import. The lesson was that exports had to pay for imports. However, the domestic prices of goods imported were higher than those paid by the licensed importer. He was therefore able to resell goods he did not need and make a fairly fat profit on the deal. This profit went to subsidise the exports. This link system did not just work for a textile manufacturer importing raw cotton and exporting cloth, it worked for imports like sugar or oil against exports of machinery and ships.

There were, of course, lots of other devices involving foreign exchange controls and tax discrimination and these various measures were so successful that in the years 1954 and 1955 export prices actually went down, leaving Japan and Switzerland unique in a world in which export prices rose everywhere else.

Nevertheless Japan could hardly feel satisfied in 1955 because over 60 per cent of her exports consisted of goods which were going to enjoy a less than average growth in world demand. By comparison only 37 per cent of Britain's exports belonged to that unhappy category. The other side of the coin meant that less than 20 per cent of Japan's exports was in goods which were going to enjoy a better than average growth in world demand, whereas in Britain's case nearly 50 per cent lay in this category. This can be said with the benefit of hindsight but market research was clearly pointing in these directions for the ten-year period from 1955 to 1965.

Japan saw the danger early, and so she brought about a drastic change in the structure of her exports. The result was that her total exports went up 320 per cent in the ten-year period, as against a 140 per cent increase in world manufactured exports. What did Britain do? Her exports increased by less than 55 per cent.

Nobody who reads the evolving story in Japan's successive economic surveys since the mid-fifties can doubt that she achieved her success by the most deliberate policies. To retail that story now involves delving into figures, but for once the figures are more illuminating than words even for the most unmathematical reader:

Table 1

Goods where growth rate in world trade 1955–64 was:	% share in Japan's exports		Japan's annual average increase in exports %	Japan's annual average increase in investment %
	1955	1964	1955–64	1955–64
Maximum	10	26	39	31
Large	9	15	23	26
Medium	17	13	16	25
Below average	43	37	9	18
Stagnant	21	8	1	15

The authors of Japan's economic survey in 1966, looking back again to the take-off period ten years before, divided Japan's principal exports, nearly a hundred categories of them, into five main groups. These were:

1. 'Maximum' export growth goods, in which total world exports and imports had more than trebled in the decade after 1955 (they included business machines, electric machinery, and several chemicals);

2. 'Large' growth goods, in which total world trade had expanded since 1955 by around two and a half times (they included several other sorts of machinery and automobiles);

3. Goods which had shown a 'medium' growth in total world trade by just about doubling since 1955 (e.g. watches, some other metallic or mineral products, inorganic compounds);

4. Goods which had shown a 'below average' growth of only somewhere around seventy-five per cent (including iron and steel products, agricultural machinery and ships); and

5. Goods in which world trade had proved to be stagnant (of which the most important for Japan were cotton textiles).

These are the five categories set down in Table 1.

It will be immediately apparent from this table that the goods in which the expansion of world trade later proved to be below average or stagnant accounted in 1955 for an alarming 43 and 21 per cent respectively of Japan's export trade; the goods in which growth later proved maximum or large for only 10 or 9 per cent respectively. It was clear to Japan's planners and most of its industrialists even in 1955 that Japan needed to switch the main weight of its export effort from goods with fairly obviously bleak prospects, especially cotton textiles and other light goods, to the industries of the new age.

The next two columns show that this was achieved. In all of these goods Japan's exports increased annually, but in the "'maximum' growth in world demand" goods they increased by a fantastic average of 39 per cent every year, and in the other categories at a declining rate down the list. It may be said that it was natural that those goods for which world demand was expanding most quickly would also be those in which Japan's exports most particularly boomed. But not, of course, to this extent. And the last column of the table is the most significant of all. In all of these export industries Japan in the decade after 1955 was increasing its investment each year at a deliberately surging rate. But in the 'maximum' new export opportunity industries, the average rate of increase in her investment reached a remarkable 31 per cent each year. It declined thereafter down the list (despite the heavy investment in the shipbuilding and iron and steel industries, down near the basement in the "'below average' increase in world demand" category, in which Japan's special success helped to keep her figure in column 2 at a somewhat out-of-trend 37 per cent).

Once again, it was to some extent natural that investment should increase most in industries where world demand increased most. But anybody who knows Japan will be aware that investment intentions were given a sharp push in the right directions by the official planners behind the scenes. Sometimes, investment was aided by Government funds from the Japan Development Bank. More important, the big commercial banks, which have absolute control over the great majority of the country's investible funds, were left in no doubt where, in the cause of fostering Japan's export revolution, it was most desirable that their lending should go.

One of the devices used to highlight the sectors where expansion was desirable was the specialisation index. The problem with indicative planning is that few people read the forecasts and any way of making them more vivid is greatly to be wished for; the specialisation index was such a way. If an industry had a specialisation index of unity, its managers could feel that they were at least pulling their weight; when say chemicals constituted 5 per cent of total world trade, and 5 per cent of Japan's total exports were chemicals too, then the specialisation index of 1, showed that they were holding their own in the world competition. When world demand for something is rising and Japan's share is not rising as fast the index falls below 1 and everybody gets worried.

These indices were part of the planner's stock in trade in the late fifties in Japan. In Britain such statistics were a novelty even in 1965 when an industrialists' league table based on the same principle caused heated discussion at the annual conference of the British Association.

Japanese statisticians produced another index, the export estrangement coefficient, which spotlights manufacturers who are being idle about exporting. This is derived from a comparison between how much a particular manufacture ranks in exports and its proportion of total output. (If cars constituted ten per cent of exports and this figure were divided by the, say, twenty per cent which represents the proportions of cars in the total industrial output then the estrangement coefficient would be 0.5.) Obviously with service industries like, say, central heating appliances or hairdressing, the figures would be meaningless but in other sectors they form something sharp and definable to argue about.

Export dependence is something else the planners worry about. Table 2 shows Japan's industries graded by their degree of dependence on exports in 1955. For example 93 per cent of the toys made in Japan in 1955 were exported, and so were 42 per cent of the cotton fabrics produced; these industries are therefore included in the first line of the table, as industries with a 'very large' dependence on exports in 1955 (with a group average of 44 per cent of total production exported in that year). Similarly in 1955 only 1½ per cent of Japan's radio and television sets were exported (it was before the transistor boom), and these goods were therefore in the 'minimum' dependence groups which had an average export dependence of 4 per cent.

Table 2

Export dependence in 1955	Ratio of Japan's production exported in 1955	1964	Annual average increase in exports % 1955	1964	Annual average basic wages £ 1955	1964	Annual average wage increase %
Very large	44	32	8		105	259	10.6
Large	23	23	15		157	351	9.9
Medium	11	9	13		184	388	8.6
Low	7	9	16		182	413	9.5
Minimum	4	7	37		216	420	7.7

Whatever the techniques used to drive up exports it must again be stressed that it is the balancing trick that matters and Japan gives just as much attention to holding imports down. Not looking into what does this would be like discussing Hamlet without mentioning the prince. 'The real reason why Japan pulls itself out of balance of payments', says a foreign businessman in Tokyo, 'isn't its push-exports policy, but the 'no import' policy of its Ministry of International Trade and Industry (MITI) which is very toughly pursued.' Another man reduced to ulcers by MITI fights liked to call it, 'The Ministry of One Way Trade'. And it is in fact true that Japan, which in 1967 was likely to have a gross national product only slightly larger than Britain's – with a very similar industrial structure – imports only one half as much. Furthermore over sixty per cent of Japan's imports are raw materials and fuel; her imports of food and manufactured goods are very low indeed.

The interesting column in Table 2 is the fourth one. The industries most dependent on exports in 1955 were the very 'low-wage' industries, often making light goods and sundry houseware in very small firms. It was obvious that Japan would soon lose its advantage as a low-wage country to neighbouring and less developed lands. As prosperity and fuller employment increased in Japan, there was bound to be some levelling up of wages; and indeed the last column shows that since 1955 wages in the most sweated industries have been increasing at an average of 10.6 per cent a year (incidentally, the total figures in columns 4 and 5 are misleading as to absolute amounts, because they ignore the huge fringe benefits, expecially in the larger firms, which can add up to a substantial part of the Japanese worker's real wage). But this only increased the desirability of switching the emphasis in Japan from the old trades to the new. Acting largely on the planners' blueprint, the switch took place.

Because of this surging, successful and continuing change in the structure of their exports, the Japanese reckon that when total world trade in manufactures increases by one per cent, they can expect their exports to increase by two per cent; they would consider they were falling behind in the race to change the nature of their economy in advance of a changing world economy if the increase went much lower than that. In other words they are trying to raise their position in the world trade league table not just maintain it as in Britain.

But this does not solve all their problems. Their difficulty is that a one per cent increase in their gross national product also leads to a more than proportional increase in their imports: not quite to a two per cent increase in imports, but getting near to it. So whenever Japan's rate of internal growth in money terms considerably exceeds the rate of growth in total world trade in manufactures, the country is liable to run into balance of payments difficulties. Since world trade in manufactures has recently been roaring along with annual increases around 5 to 9 per cent, that might not seem a grave difficulty to a country like Britain. But it has been a major problem for Japan.

It has been met by a periodic giddy swerving into stop-go policies, but of a most sophisticated kind. When trouble threatens, a sharp and sudden credit squeeze by the Bank of Japan can usually send Japanese exports soaring. The reason for this lies largely in the 'permanent tight money situation', the fact that this is an economy run so largely on IOU's. When the squeeze is imposed, 'paper gets longer', the IOU's, with which most domestic purchases as between enterprises are made, may swell from a quite normal ninety days to 'pregnancy notes' of nine or ten months' duration; moreover, at such times, the unofficial discount rate on such pregnancy paper may soar to fifteen or twenty per cent or more. In these circumstances, an export delivery, which will be paid for far more quickly on a sight bill, becomes a much more desirable delivery for enterprises to make. All the tedious arguments about whether Japanese firms sometimes 'dump' exports in such conditions become quite meaningless when this factor of quicker payment is understood. Exports at squeeze-time become much more profitable than home market sales even if export prices are fairly low. In addition, a switch to export sales in these squeezes is helped by the fact that the big trading houses are standing ready to organize such sales; this will be discussed in the chapter devoted to trading houses.

It must be remembered too that since Japanese firms cannot lay off their work force in squeeze times, they export come what may. They do not have the sort of option realised by the British Motor Corporation which sacked twelve thousand workers during the 1966 squeeze in the United Kingdom.

While other countries see battles royal between deflationists (who say that a squeeze on the domestic economy always helps exports) and expansionists (who say that by delaying modernisation it may impede them), the Japanese put their adding machines to work to report what recent and current trends seem to show. Of the enormous 26.7 increase in Japan's exports in the squeeze year of 1965, Japan's official 'Foreign Trade Report' for 1966 solemnly estimated that 32.6 per cent could have been expected anyway from the continuing long-term growth in Japan's international competitiveness due to its changing industrial structure; 21.3 per cent came from the anticipated long-term growth trend in world imports as weighted by the countries to which Japan usually traded; 12.4 per cent from the fact that these particular partner trading-countries, especially the United States, happened in 1965 to have an above-average import boom (so that this was listed as a short-term bonus whose repetition Japan should not expect); and 33.7 per cent sprang from short-term factors in Japan itself, especially 'the greater export drive resulting from the domestic supply and demand situation'. Of course, the bogus exactitude of these estimates, to a pretended place of decimals, is absurd: but, once again, the point is that Japan's planners are moved by an almost compulsive urge to have (and to show that they have) a determined quantitative grip on at least what they think they are doing. The policy that emerges from this sometimes gritty pedagogism really does tend to be more purposive than that which emerges from the much less clearly argued prejudices of Whitehall.

In food, Japan's agricultural protectionism has, disappointingly, grown worse in the last five years. Both her own consumers (who have to pay the equivalent of a large excise tax on their rice) and Australia and New Zealand (who could by now reasonably expect to be selling much more meat to Japan) have reason to complain. In manufactures, both of capital and consumer goods, many traders will again put the blame on artificial protectionism, spelt in the four letter word MITI; but there is room for argument about its extent. As this question is important for the prospects of exporters to this market, it is worth examining in detail.

The Japanese will say that their import trade is now 94 per cent liberalised, to which the proper response is '94 per cent of what?' It is true that import quotas have now been removed on 94 per cent by value of goods imported in some base period in the past, but if there were no imports of that particular commodity brought in at that base time then ninety-four per cent of nought is still nought. Some of the liberalisation has been drawn up in an over-crafty way, to which it is right to object; imports of cars are liberalised, but imports of components for cars are not. Japanese tariff rates are high – sometimes twenty or thirty per cent or more on manufactures (cars 40 per cent) – and are on occasion tied in cunningly with the internal commodity tax to hit the foreign exporter discriminately hard. For goods sold between enterprise the exporter may have to run the gauntlet of at least an unofficial campaign to buy Japanese, probably indeed an official one. On at least one product that was supposed to be liberalised, the writer heard an authenticated story of a direct request from a MITI official to Japanese industrialists not to buy it (although it is fair to add that when proof of this was provided to more senior MITI men 'it did raise a bit of a hiss'). There are restrictions on borrowing periods for imports, but I found complete disagreement, among a group of men who ought to know, whether these were a serious impediment or not. One fairly pro-Japanese foreign businessman in Tokyo (rather a rare species this) said flatly that 'nearly all these so-called discriminations against foreign goods are things which anybody with gumption can get round.'

Another explanation of Japan's low level of imports of consumer goods is worth quoting. 'It springs partly from their high interest rates, and partly from their grossly inefficient distribution system.' The argument goes like this. Take a European product at its ex-factory price. Add insurance and freight charges to the distant market of Japan. Add the Japanese tariff. Add a large mark-up for the import merchant, whether it be a big Japanese trading house or a smaller European firm in Japan; the importer will need a big margin because of the high interest-rate cost of holding stocks in Japan, and because he probably needs to employ an English-speaking and western accountancy-understanding staff. Add the Japanese commodity tax at this stage. Add other large margins for the fantastic range of Japanese wholesalers, sub-wholesalers, and perhaps sub-sub-wholesalers through whom the goods are liable to pass. Again they need a large margin because of interest charges on stock-holding, especially as the final retailer is apt to order in tiny amounts (even the biggest of Tokyo's huge department stores sometimes place an order for a dozen English ties). Add advertising costs, which for European goods are apt to be heavy.

The result of all this is that the final retail price in Japan is liable to be either around 'three times the ex-factory price in Europe' (an optimistic Englishman's guess) or else 'nearer five times it' (a pessimistic Frenchman's). A lot of the inefficiencies of distribution, which go to swell this figure, will help also to boost the price of native Japanese goods. But not to the extent of tripling and quintupling the ex-factory price.

In the context of the balance of payments, it is worthwhile mentioning the movement of capital. For many West European countries an inflow of capital, especially from the United States, helps balances to an important extent, as the 1968 cutback showed all too clearly. Britain has been getting up to £150 million a year of foreign capital and, in spite of certain misgivings, this inward flow is positively encouraged. Japan maintains a different attitude, keeping an eagle eye even on outward bound royalty and licence payments. In the past, controls on Japanese nationals travelling abroad have been severe, except for businessmen.

'Will they liberalise?' was a vigorously debated topic in 1967. Some liberalisation is a condition of membership of the Organisation for Economic Co-operation and Development (OECD) and it is also increasingly required by GATT. Large American firms are increasingly irked by having to withstand competition from Japanese imports yet being prohibited from setting up subsidiaries in Japan.

How far liberalisation will go is not yet clear but many foreign observers would say that 'what the government will do is to announce new regulations designed to try to satisfy the OECD in their wording, but designed in actual practice to keep just as much control over every foreign investor as the government finds from day to day that it wants'.

In general it seems that foreign investors will have the freedom of industries which either Japan doesn't want (making wooden clogs was one MITI joke) or which are strong enough to stand it, like shipbuilding and steel. Growth industries like car manufacturing are not going to be liberalised and Japan's balance of payments will probably never get the sort of shot in the arm that Britain's got when the Americans bought British Ford for £300 million. But then Japan manages to regulate her import-export balance so well that she doesn't need it and she also likes to keep Japanese industry in Japanese hands.

SIXTEEN

The Great Trading Houses

The great trading houses of Japan are a phenomenon at present more or less unknown in other advanced countries. Although Japan's census of distribution can be read as listing over 4,000 or over 7,000 or even, on one reading, over 30,000 trading houses (it depends which definition of the term 'wholesaler' or 'trading house' you use), there are in fact 39 sizable houses that appear in most people's lists. Through them passed 70 per cent of Japan's exports and 80 per cent of its imports last year. The eleven biggest whose names appear in the Table at present handle over 50 per cent of both exports and imports, as well as some 20 per cent of Japan's domestic wholesale trade.

The real giants each employ more than 10,000 highly skilled staff, scattered in many branch offices throughout Japan and in the world at large. It used to be said that their great power was 'essentially a colonial-type development', and that it would wane as Japan's industrial structure grew more complex. The theory was that they belonged to the age when manufacturing establishments were small, and distributors therefore relatively much more powerful. Hence the pattern that grew up in textiles, and still lives on in parts of it and some other light industries today, where a big trading concern would buy raw cotton and send it to a small spinner, buy his yarn and send it to a weaver, buy his cloth and sub-contract its making up into a finished garment to another firm, buy the garment and export it – all on a complicated mélange of IOUs, as the great organising spider at the centre of the web.

What was not foreseen was that the trading houses would continue to be such dominant figures when Japan became an importer of nuclear reactors as well as noodles, an exporter of computers as well as ribbons and toys – when it moved on into forms of trade that other countries handle by direct importing and exporting. The question therefore has to be asked whether, by accident, Japan may have seen live over from old-fashioned times a peculiar mechanism that happens also to be very apposite to the modern age: perhaps a mechanism that other countries should consider creating *de novo*, in order to aid their exports, maximise the efficiency of their imports, and help their economies along the road of advance?

There are three main ways in which, it could be argued, giant trading corporations of this kind might give a special boost to Japanese exports.

The first way is 'by acting as expert bodies in market research with offices operating in all the great trading centres of the world'. Although this may seem the most obvious argument of the three, I do not myself now regard it as the strongest: at any rate so far as scouting out the market for new products is concerned. When a trading house deals in everything from noodles to nuclear reactors, a telegram sent to the dozen or so very articulate men in its Ruritanian office, demanding an estimate of the Ruritanian market for the new Japanese product of widgets in the year ahead, is liable to get a rather fence-sitting reply (especially if those dozen men have had to look up in a dictionary what widgets are). 'There is a great difficulty in original market research by one's own people in a foreign language, in a foreign country, across a wide field,' admits one trading house leader sadly. 'It would be so much more convenient if your countries had trading houses too, so that we could ask them for a list of what things they want to import.'

Secondly, the trading houses may help Japanese exports 'by knowing what particular changes in credit and distributional and other terms are desirable from country to country, from one stage of the trade cycle to another stage of the cycle, from season to season, in order to keep existing exports flowing out.'

The advantage that Japan has secured in this respect is probably very large. There is a whole new international art here, and I suspect that Japan's possession of well-drilled teams of professionals makes it a leader in it. The point is not simply the obvious one that in so many other advanced countries small firms regard the export market as too complicated to enter, whereas in Japan trading houses can help them. The point is also that some quite sizable exporters in other countries probably do not treat the export market as complicated enough. When an individual firm exports by direct selling to the world, it may tend to feel that dealers in all countries should be treated pretty well alike 'in so far as local custom allows'; when an import agent operates only in one country he tends to dwell excessively on the custom of the trade in that country. Actually, by modifying the customs of the country favourably in some respects, and by seeking compensation in others, quite large advances in pushing exports can sometimes be made.

Thirdly, the trading houses help Japanese exports 'by standing ready to increase their inventories of exportable goods, at times when the domestic market has cooled off – and selling them out of inventory as export opportunities arise'. This is undoubtedly another big advantage that Japan has secured from its trading house system, particularly at moments when an internal squeeze has had to be imposed in order to improve its balance of payments. As this holding of idle inventories is expensive, many of the big trading houses' profits looked pretty bleary during Japan's recession (and export record) year of 1965. But a bad year for profits at the nadir of the trade cycle does not matter so much to a big Japanese trading house which is one of the major 'army units' of one of the principal bank-based business groups. This role of a buffer stockholder of exports in times of squeeze is part of the house's recognised function in the 'bank group's' system of things.

The obvious question was put to the Japanese trader who had wished that 'other countries had trading companies too, so that we could ask them for a list of what things they want to import': what was the list of things Japan would like to import, please?

In things which Japan cannot produce herself, the trading house system works at full competitive blast. In the struggle for the contract for the next two atomic power plants – these are going to be very big business in Japan – one trading house (Nissho) acts as an agent for the British Atomic Energy Authority, and others act as agents for American atomic designs, in an orgy of lobbying and salesmanship. Fantastically to a westerner, Japan's 'self-defence' forces (i.e. army, navy and air force) get their imported equipment in the same way. Almost all important overseas manufacturers of fighter planes, aircraft engines, rockets, missiles and other military equipment are represented by one or other of the general trading houses in Japan. This is partly because the doors of Government are wider open to the trading houses than to anybody else; and partly because the houses fill many of the roles such as that of 'contract administrators' which might be filled in other countries by lawyers (an unpopular profession in Japan).

In consequence of the rise of this sort of business, what might be called the 'big contract administrator' type of executive – whether in these complicated deals or in bulk contracts for raw materials – seems to be rising to the top in most of the trading houses. The man with a keen nose for making a small killing by importing some foreign consumer goods and selling it below the Japanese product's price is much less in evidence; even Japan's much-vaunted move to greater import liberalisation in 1964 did not bring many such characters to the fore.

This raised the question: is the best way for British exports into the Japanese market through these big trading concerns? For anything that is complicated, and that requires what might be called 'contract administration' work, especially if sold to the Government or the big firms, my answer would be 'yes'. I put less emphasis than others on the usual counter-arguments such as that 'it should be possible to break through Japan's enormously high distribution costs by direct selling', or that 'if you sell through the trading house of one big banking group members of other big groups won't want to buy' (they frequently do buy). The counter-argument that has more validity applies to the scale of your effort. If it is a contract for a consumer good that is liable to net the trading house only a fairly small sum each year, then a smaller agent might show more verve in pushing it. Probably the best recipe here is: find out what is the final outlet for your product in Japan; find the small Japanese wholesaler who services that outlet, the chap who actually sends a truck to it; go out to Japan yourself and offer him good credit terms (because money is generally so tight in Japan, good credit terms are a surefire way of getting him enthusiastically committed to your side). Although you will need strong nerves during the country's periodical squeezes – and may have to negotiate with MITI in order to be allowed to extend favourable credit terms beyond a certain period – you may then find that you have got the most efficient possible entrée into what, for the medium term, is probably going to be the world's most quickly growing market.

There are other roles that these great houses play in the Japanese economy, some of which they have acquired almost in a fit of absence of mind. All the leaders of the great houses whom I met were very impressive men; they are definitely emerging as among the most internationally-minded men within their big business groups, in a country where the language barrier has helped to block internationalism's spread. They are useful informants of the Government about purchasing trends, and their economic forecasting departments are growing in importance (on the whole, they seemed to me more worried about the trend of Japan's balance of payments for the last part of 1966 than the Government was). They have played a major part in scenting out new technologies abroad and importing them into Japan; if you are going to negotiate a licensing or joint venture agreement in the country, it is wise to have a trading house on your side. They have played a major role as organisers or pilots of overseas ventures by Japanese corporations; and such overseas ventures seem almost certain to grow, as Japanese businessmen take greater advantage of lower wage levels in surrounding countries to make things that are at present sub-contracted to smaller firms in Japan itself. To some extent, indeed, some of the big trading houses are taking over some of the functions fulfilled in Britain by merchant banks.

In the trading houses' traditional 'mother hen' role to Japan's smaller businesses, it has recently become possible to sense some change of trend. It is clear that during the last recession credit was cut off pretty discriminatorily to the small manufacturing enterprises who seemed least efficient, even if they were ones with which the houses had traditional ties. 'Small businesses run by young men are, in my experience, proving better than those run by older men,' said one trading house leader. 'I cut off credit to the small firms whose owners were old men spending too much of our money on geishas and loose living,' said another. And, perhaps more scientifically, 'there has only in the last few years been a growth of a reliable system of credit risks reporting and analysis in Japan; previously, we relied too much on published accounts which with too many small businesses contained inaccuracies designed to fool the tax collector.' Underlying all this, however, there does seem to be an emerging feeling that this whole 'mother hen' system, looking after little chicks, is becoming rather an incongruous one for organisations that are also importing nuclear reactors. 'Looking after trade in small sundry goods requires a different sort of expertise and staff from that used in most of our more modern contract administration work,' one trader even essayed, 'and it is a serious question whether we should not set up a separate and subsidiary company to handle it.'

If this happened, it would be the opposite of the trend that some others have forecast for the trading houses, and with them for virtually the entire set-up of really big business in Japan: namely, a succession of mergers until eventually nearly everything was in the hands of only four giant groups. The present structure can best be examined via the Table (p.165), which lists the thirteen biggest general traders by reference to their total sales in the six months to March, 1966. The first two names, Mitsui and Mitsubishi, need cause no surprise. In next place, the third of the 'Big M's', Marubeni-Iida, is...well, now, one comes to the problem of whether to call it the big trading house attached to the Fuji bank's group. Much of the Japanese press writes as though it were. Other traders deny it, because both Marubeni and Fuji spread their business widely; but, particularly since 1965, the relations between Marubeni and Fuji have been close.

In the fourth place, C. Itoh, one of the pioneers of the trading house movement, traditionally keeps itself independent of any one group; but Sumitomo is one of its great and good friends – and the indefatigable forecasters of mergers constantly point out that if it ever merged with Sumitomo's own trading house (the rapidly growing Sumitomo Shoji, still down at seventh place, but only because a major trading house was not in Sumitomo's original scheme of things), then the domination of the trading field by the four pre-war zaibatsu (Mitsui, Mitsubishi, Sumitomo, and Fuji-once-called-Yasuda) would really be complete.

The vigour of the trading houses just a little smaller than the big four casts considerable doubt on these forecasts. All of them are associated in some way with one of the big banks. In fifth place Toyo Menka has close ties with the Tokai bank, from Nagoya City; at sixth, Nichimen can be called even more flatly the central trading company of the group of enterprises collected around the Sanwa bank; at eighth, Nissho, although it spreads its borrowing, has the Dai-ichi bank as its partner in many enterprises. Some people even talk of the growth of a new group. The Bank of Tokyo, which as a semi-official institution would prefer to keep above group-building, has lately had to take the initiative in merging Gosho (a trading company specialising largely in textiles, which was hard hit by the 1965 recession) with F. Kanematsu, another house which borrows largely from the Bank of Tokyo. Other big trading houses mentioned in the table, or among the other 26 sizable trading companies just outside it, are often specialists in particular products, or in effect the trading departments of big firms that prefer to keep outside one of the major bank groups in their sales activities, or sometimes virtually affiliates of the big groups themselves. For example, American – and Chinese – touchiness about people who trade with communist China sometimes makes it advisable to hive off this business into a separate company; the Chinese then regard the subsidiary as a friendly house (even though they must know that it is really the foster-child of a big group), and the Americans can regard the big group as pure and un-contaminated (even though they must know that it has this foster-child).

	Half-yearly sales proceeds Oct. 1965 – March 1966
Mitsui	777
Mitsubishi Shoji	743
Marubeni-Iida	583
C. Itoh	575
Toyo Menka	325
Nichimen	280
Sumitomo Shoji	257
Nissho	245
Chori	185
Iwai	167
F. Kanematsu*	162
Ataka	151
Gosho*	107

* F. Kanematsu and Gosho are in the process of a merger.

What are the general conclusions to be drawn from this peculiar, but very efficient, system? There are, perhaps, four main ones. First, the role played by the giant trading houses does spring partly from Japan's unusual business structure with its emphasis on interlocking groups of enterprises; but it would be a great mistake to regard this as the houses' only *raison d'être*.

Secondly, one should note the remarkable separation between the production and the marketing functions in Japan. The system whereby most big manufacturing firms regard their job as being to concentrate on productive efficiency and modern-isation of products, and then ship out the whole output to some wholesaler whose job is to try to sell it, offends against a lot of orthodox business ideas in the West; but it has led, in these days of mass-production and of constant changes in production techniques, to some surprising advances in manufacturing

165

efficiency, even though it may also in some degree have failed to maximise consumers' welfare by as much as a more orthodox western system would have done.

Thirdly, if any other country set up these giant trading corporations, which are experts both in what is wanted on their domestic markets and in what is being done abroad, then they might make a quick profit by bringing in foreign goods that domestic producers are not yet making so well. But in Japan what is more likely to happen is that advice is passed on down the line on how Japan had better promptly improve its own manufacture of these goods.

Fourthly, in exports, the giant trading corporations have brought smaller advantages than might have been expected in market research; bigger advantages in an understanding of the selling techniques needed in different countries; and a very large advantage indeed in the fact that during a squeeze any large manufacturer making anything which cannot be sold at home passes it on automatically into the inventories of the trading houses, with the hope that they will be able to sell it somewhere in the world market (which, since Japanese ex-factory prices are competitive, they very often can). In addition, the Japanese hope that the present 3 per cent of their trading houses, sales which consist of 'third country business' (e.g. sales of German chemicals to Ghana) will increase. Their feeling here is that, in salesmanship as in manufacturing, the future lies with the big international firms – and they have the biggest international trading corporations *in situ*, in a growing number of markets round the world.

SEVENTEEN

Planners, People, Statistics

In one sense it has been easier for Japan to go ahead with a faster rate of growth than other industrialised countries, because the way ahead is already charted. By looking to other countries Japan can predict the sort of capacities she will need in basic industrial commodities and she can also work out the ideal disposition of labour and the productivity it ought to be achieving.

The great process of Japanese economic growth has consisted of an exercise in pushing resources out of the low productivity 'ancient' sector of the economy into the high productivity 'modernised' sector. This has gone on at great speed in spite of the fact that her lifetime employment system makes such pushing far more difficult than in any other country in the world. One of the surprises for the visitor inquiring into the facts of the employment situation in Japan is that, in spite of a deluge of instant statistics, the most familiar figure of all by which we measure the nation's health, is one quite difficult to get. In fact it will be a very subtle reply that greets the question; what is the rate of unemployment in Japan?

The reason for this is that the Japanese regard Western-style unemployment statistics as nonsense. The sort of figures which they think that planners need are the kind set down in the following Table from Japan's Economy Survey for 1964.

Buried in the list there is indeed a figure which does correspond to the 'wholly unemployed'. But were this figure to fall very low, there would not necessarily be a cry that the economy

	Total for male and female in 1,000 persons		
	1956	1959	1962
Total number of persons seeking employment	5,715	5,128	4,947
1. No. of almost totally unemployed persons	2,598	2,246	1,303
(a) totally unemployed	868	803	402
(b) just graduated from school	428	348	254
(c) not totally unemployed but having a hard time making a living	1,302	1,095	647
2. No. of persons employed, but desiring new work	3,100	2,859	3,643
(a) No. of persons with leisure time on hand	1,002	1,009	974
(b) Those who want to earn tuition fees and pocket money	2,098	1,850	892
(c) Those who have no difficulty in making a living, but desire to increase their incomes	—	—	1,777

(Based on Prime Minister's Office's 'Basic Survey of the Employment Structure')

was overheated and running short of labour. For example, in 1962 when Japan's expansionist policies had greatly reduced the number of workers in what might be called the 'poverty stricken' employment-seeking categories, the planners promptly added another 1.8 million to the total potential employment seekers by including a new category 2, c. In an advancing country, the definition of what are possibly willing movers from low wage jobs in relatively unproductive industries needs to be constantly adjusted.

One of Japan's economic planners talks about the problem like this: 'On the whole we've clearly gained through not relying on western-style unemployment statistics. In the last years of the occupation which coincided with the Korean war, some American advisers said that we were reflating irresponsibly, and running into a labour shortage. But it was obvious from the miserable jobs so many Japanese were still doing that we were really still an underemployed society. So we continued with the policy of pumping in more demand, but recognised that we would have to stop when a labour shortage really appeared. However, as we did so, our definition of a real labour shortage kept on changing too. The first assumption was that – because of our wage-for-age and lifetime-employment system, which makes entrepreneurs want to recruit only school-leavers – the point of full employment would be reached when all school-leavers could get a more or less decent job. That point was reached in the late 1950s; and it is true that thereafter the policy of pumping in still more demand began to run into difficulties, including much higher rates of price inflation. But it still seemed right to us to keep on pumping in more demand. By doing so, it proved possible to draw more people into what I would call the effective labour force in the modern sector of industry; to push up the retirement age from the previous ridiculously low age of fifty-five, and to get some people to move from unproductive firms to more productive firms, even when they were not necessarily young. My own private estimate is that we can profitably go on with our policy of pumping up total demand, and still get a useful response in the labour market, for another five years. After that, our really high rates of growth may have to stop because by then we really may run into a genuine labour shortage – unless, of course, by then we have managed to carry out other sociological or economic reforms so that we can again drastically change our conception of what a labour shortage, or what a relatively unproductive industry due for decline, really means.'

Before going on to look at the way Japan plans to tackle the expected embarrassments of being rich, it may be as well to look back a few years to get some idea of the pace at which it has moved from being a pre-industrial society, and also to look at the sort of experience that life has given to Japanese workers. This will help to explain what sort of flesh and blood lies behind the economists' figures.

In 1937 agriculture, forestry and fishing accounted for about forty per cent of Japan's working population. The rest, around eighteen million, were nominally employed in manufacturing establishments but only about two million or so seem to have worked in firms employing more than fifty people. Japan provided a good example of what it has now become fashionable to call 'intermediate technology' and it was easy for labour to flow back to agriculture in times of recession. In the textile industry in particular young women workers came mainly from peasant families and returned to their homes after as little as three years' employment. Only a small portion of the total working population could be regarded as permanent wage-earners, and the thirties (in which Japan suffered severe deflation) passed largely undisturbed by Jarrow marches or by the bitter battles which have so deeply marked the British labour movement.

Lest it be thought that thirty years ago Japan enjoyed a golden age of agrarian tranquillity, such as the English suppose is their lost heritage, a sort of eighteenth-century squirearchy with good harvests and hot summers, it must be remembered that there were many severe famines all over Japan with rural families living on a pound a month or just over a penny a day each in 1932 and 1933. In central Japan rural families were so poor that girls were sold into prostitution. A contemporary account of conditions in Japan's coal mines reads like an account of English conditions a hundred years previously; not only were women and children at work in them but chained prisoners undertook forced labour and further reduced wage levels which were already very low. The then boss of Mitsui, the Finance Minister and the Prime Minister were all murdered and yet, somehow, these years did not produce the really bitter, tough, old-time Trade Union leadership which became the legacy of the thirties for Britain.

When a visiting British Union leader looks a shipyard worker in the eye seeking some sign of brotherhood, he does not see a man who can say proudly and stubbornly, 'I'm doing the job my father did before me, and what was good enough for him is good enough for me.' His Japanese father and his grandfather were almost certainly rural peasants living in Asiatic poverty thirty years ago. This fact, coupled with the total devastation of all Japan's industrial capacity by 1946, has meant that for most Japanese workers the idea of the 'two sides of industry' means nothing, and there is no long tradition of two separate camps, the workers and the bosses, endlessly wrangling over the division of what are essentially static earnings. Instead there has been a giddy surge within recent memory, in which earnings have gone up and up, doubling every ten years; and in which new skills have continually had to be learnt until, at least in many Japanese firms, productivity per worker is ahead of the West's.

The thirties were bad, but as a memory they are not a significant part of the industrial tradition and they did not form the kind of soil on which militant trade unionism could flourish. Even in 1955, forty per cent of Japan's labour force was still in agriculture, forestry and fishing, but by 1965 this had fallen by nearly a half. In 1965 the decrease was about 390,000 a year, so agriculture is still serving, though on a diminishing scale, as a reservoir of labour for manufacturing industry.

There are, however, several strange features of the Japanese labour scene in which many observers see relics not only of an agricultural past, but of a feudal society.

The first is the celebrated paternalism of the Japanese employer. This has been compared to the feudalism which Japan left only a century ago; workers are imagined to function as if they were unquestioning serfs in an industrial enterprise which is a substitute for a warlord's fiefdom.

There is some truth in this picture, but it is changing. On leaving school or university, would-be workers apply to the firm of their choice, and the big ones, Mitsubishi, Hitachi and so on, get the cream. They even run their own exams. Once inside, a lifetime's secure employment stretches ahead with pay increases coming by age rather than by ability. This is not to say that there is no differential between jobs, but within any category, the older you are, the more you get. One side effect of this is that it gives a concealed subsidy to a new young industry, because its young staff will be very cheap and very good. The older a firm is, however, the higher its labour costs, and this is one solid reason behind the selection of 55 as retirement age. There is also a disadvantage to the worker, for should he want to move he must do so early, since the longer he leaves it, the less he will be able to stand the drop in salary. He will, of course, begin at the bottom of the ladder again, paid according to the years he has spent with his new firm, rather than by his own age. This kind of consideration applies even to top graduates who find in it a strong disincentive against going to the United States for experience. If they do go they may have to stay because, unless they come to work for a foreign firm in Japan, they will have to start at the bottom of the ladder if they do decide to come back.

For its 'regular workers' the Japanese company is capable of providing anything from nurseries to holiday camps and golf club subscriptions, from geisha parties to hospitals and medical treatment, and especially houses. It goes without saying that the company provides training for new staff and retraining for any workers whom it requires to move to other kinds of employment within the firm. According to its critics, the Japanese company provides a cradle to grave service, with the boss attending the weddings and the children born in the company maternity home, but it denies individuals their freedom and denies the economy the benefits of a free labour market. On the other hand, since Japanese companies never sack their workers they can claim an astonishing loyalty, and when it comes to installing an automated machine the unions co-operate.

Another reason the unions co-operate is that they are plant unions, not craft unions; demarcation disputes are very rare, and so is the kind of wage drift which is caused by a union's determination to maintain differentials against other classes of worker. The plant union system only causes trouble when it comes to getting companies to merge completely. Recently, as mentioned in Chapter 2, in the motor industry, Toyota and Hino negotiated a tie-up instead of a merger, largely because of the difficulties of merging the separate plant unions. There are 51,000 different unions with over nine million members and, as the Japanese statisticians point out, the percentage of organised labour for Japan is 36.3 per cent, as against 43.6 for Britain, 29.7 for the United States and 35.4 per cent for West Germany.

They do go on strike; there were over two thousand disputes involving nearly eight million workers in 1964 for instance. Present-day Japanese unions cannot be said to be militant; the only exceptions are the mining unions in Hokkaido where, in a declining industry, one bitter strike marked by violence lasted for twenty-two months. These are probably areas where memories of the thirties do remain, and memories too of the suppression of the unions in 1937.

After the War, during the American occupation, three laws were passed establishing the rights of Trades Unions. In the late forties, these unions went through a phase of extreme militancy and the government curtailed many newly-won privileges. Civil servants and railway workers, for example, were denied the right to strike, though collective bargaining was allowed to continue. Once Japan entered into its period of sustained economic growth, however, the unions became docile. And, provided prosperity continues, Japanese workers are likely to remain docile either in unions or out of them. Wouldn't anyone whose income doubled every eight years, even without promotion?

The key phrase, is however, 'provided prosperity continues.' No one knows what would happen to the mood of Japanese labour if economic stagnation set in, but it reasonable to suspect that many of the 'English diseases' could quite easily appear in Japan. The one thing the economic planners are determined to avoid is any really prolonged stop on the upward spiral so that, with any luck, Japanese susceptibility to English diseases will never have to be tested.

Once the supply of fresh labour stops flowing from agriculture the Japanese economy will face a new situation. In similar classic situations other countries have found that the shortage of labour forces up wages, prices rise, exports fall, imports flood in and expansion has to stop. This is the well-known stop-go disease, one of the best known of the English economic maladies. In Japan there will be no shortage of highly educated labour; in 1967 a number of university graduates had to take jobs which they considered to be 'not of the university graduate type'. The shortage will be of unskilled labour. Faced with a similar situation West Germany escaped by importing foreign labour from Greece, Italy and Spain. Japan could follow a simiar course by importing Chinese from Taiwan, or Koreans, or Malays, or Filipinos. The Japanese, however, are a very proud people and the prospect of diluting Japanese culture with foreigners meets with this sort of response, 'Nobody here would tolerate the prospect of giving up the great advantage we have enjoyed all through history in the homogeneity of our Japanese people.' It must also be pointed out that the country is overcrowded enough already, and Japan has no wish to repeat the example of Britain where, no sooner was part of the working class lifted off the bottom and out of its slums than a new class of coloured under-privileged was imported in its place.

'A more likely alternative', said one observer, 'might be to move Japanese capital to foreign countries instead of moving foreign workers into Japan. Big Japanese firms at present sub-contract a lot of the task of making components to small firms with unskilled workers, in Japan itself. More and more of these subcontracting firms may set up with Japanese capital and enterprise in Korea and Taiwan. That could be the pattern of the future.'

It was also, of course, the pattern of the past represented by the notorious Greater Asian Co-prosperity Sphere, which was the aim of Japanese policy at the beginning of the Pacific war. Memories of the Japanese occupation are long, however, and it will need more than goodwill visits from Mr Sato to allay the lingering deep suspicions of Japan. Nevertheless the democratic Japan of today appears to be less of a threat to new nationhood and rather more of a sympathetic source of capital and know-how. In the near future, overseas investment by Japan seems sure to grow and it will provide both a solution to Japan's labour shortage and a welcome boost for the developing countries of South East Asia.

Another way out will be automation. One has only to see Japanese management eyeing new gadgets and experimenting with computers to realise that this solution to the problem is likely to dominate the others. Japanese labour will be given more and more machinery to augment its productive ability, and the planners are already studying ways to help this process along.

'Investment', declared Japan's Economic Survey for 1966, 'might be divided into two types – one, expansion investment which simply aims at stepping up production volume, and the other intensive investment, which is designed to raise "capital volume per worker", in order to save scarce labour. And then, with the statistician's bravery so characteristic of modern Japan, the survey goes on to estimate that 'the ratio between the two in Japan in 1955–61 was seven to three, with extensive investment conspicuously rising above intensive investment, but in 1961–4 the ratio was two to eight.'

This estimate may not be correct but the mere fact that it has been made shows, again, the great driving urge in Japan for economic planners to get some sort of a quantitative grip on what they think the country ought to be doing. Trying to influence the ratio between extensive and intensive investment is not going to be easy but the Japanese are tackling it years in advance of countries like Britain which, with a much tighter labour situation, has much greater need to do so.

EIGHTEEN

The Human Factor

A crude but illuminating way of approaching the question 'what makes a nation tick?' is to examine the folk myths or the lives of national heroes. If a visiting anthropologist looked at the British in this way he would be struck perhaps by the wide variety of the folk myths. Robin Hood is obviously one, a man who robbed the rich to pay the poor. Furthermore the whole nation forgave him for it. Next perhaps would be Robert the Bruce who fought so tenaciously for the freedom of Scotland. Other heroes like Francis Drake and Nelson fought great battles and won them from positions of weakness. Wellington who had enough troops at Waterloo is regarded with less affection. Lady Godiva was another notable figure on the side of the underdog and King Arthur, if not exactly fighting for the poor, stood for a tradition of Christian charity woven with chivalry, a passion for justice and an exaltation of romantic love. These figures embody characteristics the English admire.

The French have Joan of Arc, who, like so many great French heroes, fought against the oppressors and lost. The Americans have exalted their national leaders like Lincoln and Washington. It was the latter who is popularly supposed to have said, 'I cannot tell a lie', and the esteem in which they are both held emphasises the American devotion to liberty. The list can easily be amplified and although it is a most imprecise and unscientific way of accounting for national character, itself a dangerously loose concept, one can understand its attractions for pioneer anthropologists. In the absence of any more scientific ways of measuring and describing what it is that motivates the Japanese, what makes them different from people in other countries, no apologies will be offered for setting down their most popular national story as a point of departure.

The story in question is that of the Forty-seven Ronin. It is often said that, whenever a Japanese film company is on the rocks, the cry goes up in the boardroom: 'Let's make the Forty-seven Ronin again.' This is regarded as a sure way of packing the cinemas and restoring the company's fortune. It should be explained at once that western readers who expect something like the William Tell, Robin Hood, Davy Crockett stories will be surprised.

Like most national epics it is founded on fact, on an incident that happened at the beginning of the eighteenth century. At that time effective power in Japan was held by the Shogun who was a military ruler, the Emperor being, so to speak, on the shelf. The Shogun ran a court and had gathered a hierarchy around him. A certain Lord Asano Takuminokami was appointed to a governorship in the place of the retiring Lord Kira Koosukensuka. Lord Kira thought little of the upstart Asano and did his best to humiliate him. The most dramatic incident occurred at the Shogun's court itself, when Kira sneered publicly at Asano's lack of etiquette; one version of the story makes it sound as if Kira actually made Asano turn up, as it were, in a dinner jacket when everyone else was in tails.

The whole thing appears to have started because Asano did not give Kira the right presents. However, so compelling were the conventions of correct behaviour in Japan that the scene was set for tragedy. Asano was bound by obligation to his own name to avenge the insult, but was equally bound by obligation to the Shogun not to draw his sword. The only way out was to kill Kira and then commit suicide. Unfortunately Asano muffed the killing but was nevertheless obliged to commit hara kiri.

One might have thought that, since the principle that people shall be bent before convention had been adequately demonstrated, the matter would end there, but not so. Asano had three hundred Samurai retainers who were now leaderless. Convention required that they too should commit hara kiri and most of them did. Some of them however appear to have shown the glimmerings of understandable human response by deciding that before they committed suicide, at least they would fix Lord Kira. These were the forty-seven Ronin.

To that end, and to the everlasting enjoyment of Japanese theatre and cinema audiences, they set about lulling Lord Kira's bodyguard into relaxing its vigilance. Some of them hit the bottle and broke numerous strict conventions, dishonouring themselves in public. One sold his wife to a brothel, another let his sister become Kira's concubine (she was a spy) and they all gave up sword practice which, for a samurai, is worse than a footballer pawning his boots or a baseball player his bat. A particularly savoury moment comes when one of the forty-seven Ronin, in order to demonstrate his utter disloyalty and moral disintegration, kneels down to eat raw fish pieces held between the toes of one of Lord Kira's Samurai. This sort of thing goes on for two years until one snowy night they all meet in an eating house in Tokyo and ready themselves to storm Kira's castle. In one giant battle Kira's bodyguard is wiped out and Lord Kira himself is found cowering in a coal cellar. They spear him to death, cut off his head and carry it off to a Buddhist temple near Osaka where the grisly relic is humbled before the decomposing head of their erstwhile master Lord Asano. And then? Well, of course, they all commit hara kiri, including the luckless sister who had been deputed to be Lord Kira's concubine.

Why is it that present-day Japanese still consider this story wholly heroic? The temple and the heroes' graves are virtually a national shrine. The reason is that the need to discharge social obligations, and the need never to lose face, epitomised by the story, are the cardinal motives of Japanese social life.

Now both these motivations are of course present in the West, although loss of face is of declining importance. In Japan however both of them really matter. If, for example, you ask a Western resident to arrange an introduction and interview for you with a high Japanese personage, it is quite possible that you will be told that although Mr Itsibishi does owe Mr Smith a good deal of 'on', Mr Smith does not feel that he ought to spend this 'on' on you. This happened to the writer at least twice although in each case, either by charm or persistence, the interviews were subsequently arranged. I expected, when Mr Smith took me to meet Mr Itsibishi that the relationship between them would be affable and distant, like that between partners to a business deal where one owes the other money or favour. But in both cases the relationship was as close and familiar as that between the very best of friends in the West. Only then did it become clear that this minute accounting of debit and credit in obligations goes to the core of Japanese social life. Whereas in the West, deep friendship will exist even when the passage of favours and goods is largely one way, people in Japan will actually avoid the spontaneous gesture of giving someone a present because they would also be dispensing an obligation to reciprocate, and this might be difficult. In that case doing a favour or giving a present would actually be tantamount to saddling a person with a debt.

In traditional Japanese society a man grows up in a web of obligations, first to his parents for bringing him up, then to his teachers and employers, then to his family and to the Emperor. Other obligations are incurred during the course of life and all are repaid or discharged on the basis of *quid pro quo*. These obligations are taken very seriously for two reasons. The first is the early and intensive conditioning of children, and the second is the lack of any idea of the transcendental in Japanese religions. First, conditioning: it may be due to overcrowding or to living in paper houses but there is little sign of uninhibited behaviour in Japanese children when it comes to paying respect, shutting up and bowing to elders. Nor is destructive behaviour tolerated, and a great premium is put on lying still when supposed to be asleep and not crying out when in pain. The influence of Dr Spock has not yet materially affected these spartan traditions. In many other respects Japanese children are much less inhibited and grow up with much more relaxed attitudes, to sex and drink for example. Western visitors often find adult Japanese tycoons a puzzling mosaic of spartanism and hedonism. In the middle of a geisha binge which would shock a Puritan rigid, it is quite possible to be shown a moxa scar. These result from burning chrysanthemum leaves into the skin, a very painful practice which has been widely used as a corrective in schools. Even adult tycoons still practise it to prove their self-control.

So deep is the conditioning that even Japanese mental patients remain docile and need never be locked up. Before the occupation, loyalty to the Emperor was so fanatically inculcated that in schools, even when the photograph of the Imperial Family was merely being moved from, say, a storehouse to the platform in the school assembly hall, the national anthem was played on loudspeakers and children in distant classrooms had to leap to attention whilst the icon was on the move. There are even cases of headmasters committing suicide after their schools had been burnt down with the accidental inclusion of the Imperial photograph, even though they could in no way be blamed. It is small wonder that when, after the Pacific War, General MacArthur was photographed wearing an open-necked shirt and smoking a corn-cob pipe with the Emperor beside him, Japan sagged with the shock. This would not have surprised anyone who knew MacArthur of course; it would have made no difference if the Emperor had been God himself. As the US Army song put it, when MacArthur died the first words he would utter on entering heaven would be, 'Move over God it's Mac'.

On that irreverent note it is appropriate to ask if the Japanese have any idea of a God, whose significance transcends earthly life. The short answer is that they have not. This hampered early Christian missionaries who could only communicate their doctrine by using the word Kami which implies a very powerful leader. This does not mean that the Japanese have no sense of the numinous; they can be superstitious and have an acute awareness of spirits, particularly ancestral spirits. Their attitude is nevertheless fairly casual; at a Shinto shrine for example there is little of that devout reverence displayed by serious Catholics in the presence of the Host. At Shinto shrines they ring a bell and clap hands loudly to summon the spirits and then throw them a coin.

Buddhism is even more confusing. Whilst the Indian variety almost shades into something parallel to Christianity with its concept of a heavenly Nirvana and the feeling that life here on earth is only a pale reflection of the true reality, the Zen Buddhism popular in Japan exalts intuition and provides an antidote to the strict conventions of everyday life. Instead of forever striving to perfection, man is encouraged to relax and liberate the inner self. Zen has no holy writ and the advice of the original Lord Buddha does not survive as a guide to conduct.

Moral imperatives in Japan do not, as in the West, stem from abstract principles or the teachings of allegedly supernatural personalities. Moral imperatives come from other people here on earth, other Japanese to whom obligations are owed.

This is an important and fundamental feature of the Japanese approach to life and death. Suicide is no crime; it wipes the record clean after failure, it closes the book with a proud bang and even twenty years ago hara kiri was something to be done with style. A well-known Japanese modern novelist writes with admiration of a wartime admiral who disembowelled himself in the approved way with one lateral and one upward stroke of his own sword. Unfortunately he did not die immediately but he did maintain the correct pose, contemplating his protruding intestines until, after several hours, death released him. Fortunately modern Japanese youth is beginning to feel that the Forty-seven Ronin and the latter-day militarists may have got life a little out of focus. The suicide rate in Japan is currently below that of Austria and Sweden although the overall figures may conceal a high rate of youthful suicides. Exposure to the west has also helped. Although it is not be to recommended, it is possible to press on the cracks in the Japanese national character by asking those with whom you are sufficiently friendly whether there are still circumstances in which they would commit suicide whilst of sound mind. The response is likely to be embarrassment, which is a heartening sign.

What has all this got to do with Japan's economic miracle? The reason for this lengthy digression is the need to explain the kind of motives which the individual worker feels. The ordinary machine operative has been brought up in an atmosphere of deference to authority, he has the feeling that he must excel simply in loyalty to his own name. Criticism causes him extreme distress and is to be avoided, and he is willing to work long hours for the larger community to which he belongs. People are proud to work for a particular firm, and if an order is likely to be delayed they will feel personally obliged to rescue the situation. The fact that lifetime employment is the tradition also helps in calling forth this loyalty.

This close family atmosphere means that a company can be very agile in its response to changing situations and it also means that new and more efficient methods of work can be introduced without the sort of protests common in European countries. The workers do not automatically think that the benefits of more efficient working will accrue only to the bosses; that their status, which is based on age rather than skill, will be diminished, that redundancy will result.

These group loyalties are deeper in Japan than they are in other countries because the Japanese worker's view of life is so simple. In the mind of a worker in the west there are all sorts of half-accepted political and ethical ideas, that the workers should unite against the bosses, that all men are equal and ought to be paid the same, that, as one Trades Union leader puts it, profits are wage rises the workers did not get, that 'fair shares for all' is more important than investment, that a man must stick by his principles even to the extent of bankrupting his company by a strike and so on. The tradition of craft unionism rather than plant unionism further divides a European worker's loyalty.

In Japan, group loyalties have not only helped individual firms, they have also been the source of intense competition between the ex-zaibatsu rivals, and this has greatly benefited

Japan. Incidentally, loyalty to Japan herself has been a potent factor in encouraging exports whilst discouraging imports. It is obviously and unquestionably patriotic to buy Japanese, and the Government has no need to offend other nations by saying so publicly.

Finding out what really makes workers tick in Japanese industry is of course a perfectly justifiable piece of research and indeed such a study is just beginning at London University. The intention is to compare three Japanese factories with three British ones and the results will be eagerly awaited, at least in Britain. Until more and better sociological studies are available, it is possible only to speculate on why the world's two major offshore islands are at opposite ends of the economic growth league tables. Recalling the national folk myths, perhaps one could say that what is wrong with the British is too much Robin Hood; that is to say that British political and social attitudes are essentially concerned with sharing out fairly between rich and poor a constant amount of material wealth. The idea that certain persons or organisations should be allowed to accumulate such wealth so that it may be productively invested to produce more wealth has not been properly grasped.

There is no reason to believe that there is any fundamental link between the economic activity of investing and building up technology, and living the good life. Only the Methodists have achieved a fusion of good business and good religion and their stern creed is not sweeping the world. The leading marks of Western civilization are essentially concerned with non-material values, like freedom of individual expression, the rule of law and political liberty. These concepts are derived from the laws of nature only in the most circuitous way, and it cannot be considered surprising that they may actually hamper the speedy erection of a new chemical plant or radical reductions in the price of steel per ingot ton. Nations of people who submit to authority but retain just enough initiative to work well when it is required, have shown that they are generally better at building the economic apparatus required to raise material standards of living. The Germans and the Japanese are outstanding examples.

Their success impels other nations to attempt to stay in the same league. Ways of life which are economically unsuccessful will not survive.

This does not mean that the British must work like ants, and do physical exercises before singing the company song when the day's toil begins (though these exercises of zeal are wearing off in Japan). It does mean that the British are faced with an example which they know can be emulated. The Japanese objective is to raise the standard of living of millions of people who are too poor to live the good life; the life that those of the British who are cultured enough to understand feel is the sort of life a free man should be able to live. For poor countries like India, Japan is a shining beacon that proves that it is possible to rise out of Asiatic poverty within a measurable span of years. India, after all, is full of natural resources and in this respect she is far better off than Japan ever was.

The Japanese ethical code is slowly being modified under the impact of ideas from the west and Communism, and the strain of operating an industrialised economy. The concept of social justice, for example, is taking hold. Although the poverty of the mining areas of Hokkaido is, strictly speaking, nobody's problem except the local politicians', Japan's instant mass-communications industry has brought such problems to every-one's notice in a most immediate way. Widespread sympathy is aroused and there is the political will to do something about the region in spite of there being no obvious obligation. Such diseases of city growth as pollution make it apparent that individual groups cannot carry on their business without some sense of generalised social responsibility. This sort of development is not before its time because the Japanese are particularly irresponsible when it comes to destroying natural amenities. Their own coastline is being ruthlessly exploited and its natural beauty destroyed, and the way the Japanese have behaved at conferences called to restrain the whaling industry before certain species are hunted to extinction, is a disgrace to any civilised nation.

On the labour front there are signs that the lifelong employment system is breaking down and that loyalty to the firm is weakening. Some industry bosses even go so far as to advocate trimming labour forces to a firm's needs. At IHI and Toshiba they actually do so.

The younger Japanese are beginning to find the form at Matsushita Electric for example faintly amusing. For the executives, work begins with prayers and a twenty-minute tea ceremony on the days the founder, Konosuka Matsushita, comes in. For everybody, the next item is the company song which burst on an astonished world in Time magazine in 1962.

> *For the building of new Japan*
> *Let's put our strength and mind together*
> *Doing our best to promote production.*
> *Sending our goods to the people of the world*
> *Endlessly and continuously*
> *Like Water gushing from a Fountain.*
> *Grow Industry, grow, grow, grow.*
> *Harmony and Sincerity!*
> *Matsushita Electric!*

Matsushita is not the only firm to turn its inner aspirations into song. Nissan and Toyota have also got inspirational anthems with lines like 'it's sweat and grease, for the joy of man'. When these loyal sentiments subside it is unlikely that Japan will swing to the opposite extreme. For one thing group loyalty has been too successful to be thrown over completely and for another the roots of the Japanese national character run very deep indeed.

NINETEEN

Conclusion

In a book of this kind, no chapter is more difficult to write than the last one. Some sort of summary is called for, a drawing together of threads and a tentative prediction as to the future.

'If you were asked to put your finger on one outstanding reason for Japan's success, what would it be?' This was a question put to me one evening after I returned from Japan. I had been deeply involved in the intricacies of particular industries and the exact role of MITI in this and that, so I replied without much thought: 'Oh, certainly, the very high standard of the civil servants and the fact that they all want Japan to grow . . . ' Then someone, a man concerned with importing Japanese cars into Britain, said that he thought it was because Japanese businessmen were able to keep their rewards instead of losing them in tax. He mentioned that he had been on a tastefully-furnished yacht on the Inland Sea. I said that it must have been a company yacht because personal taxation was as high as in Britain. 'Ah, but the fringe benefits . . . ' said someone else, and so it went on. I realised immediately that I simply could not put my finger on one particular reason. The civil service was numerate and of high calibre but another essential feature was that industrialists co-operated with it and trusted it. Immediately the attitude of the workers came to mind and then the plant unions, the bonuses put in the bank, the high investment, the IOUs and a host of other factors. As in an ecological system, everything depends on the growth of everything else. No one would try to summarise what happens to all living creatures in a field or a wood when the spring rains and warmer sunshine set the yearly cycle in motion again, and it seems equally unprofitable to try to summarise an economy of a hundred million people.

In a sense, the education drive a hundred years ago at the end of the Tokugawa Shogunate was such a prime cause. Education indeed is currently in favour with economists as the philosopher's stone of economic development at all stages of evolution. But here again the history of Japan confounds conventional wisdom. In many developing countries literacy drives and primary education have merely prompted people to leave the countryside and plunge into the towns, creating tragic slums. Japanese education did not do this for reasons to do with family authority, love of the land and other factors which merit a book to themselves, and indeed the book has already been written by Professor Dore at London University.

Again, Japanese education today is not startlingly different from education in other developed countries. In the fifties, for example, Japan spent six per cent of her GNP on education, while Britain spent five per cent. Japanese children leave school at fifteen after nine compulsory years and may then go to a wide range of high schools and colleges. Vocational training is widely emphasised and retraining is on a larger scale than in Britain. But it is difficult to say how much of this is special investment as opposed to a normal response to demand.

One thing is undeniable, the Japanese are very keen on education. Even pre-war there was a popular song which went: 'I'll give my daughter's hand to a university graduate.' Competition to get into the universities is very fierce and, in general, education is seen as the most important way ahead. David Reisman tells a horrific story about Hokkaido in his book, *Conversations in Japan*. 'As young as seven or eight, children started work at five in the morning, studied until seven, when it was time to leave for the public school, and they returned at three for further study. If they didn't do their lessons they were beaten by the headmaster ... the regimen might be defensible; for Hokkaido was poor, the children going to public school could not hope to get into the University of Tokyo or the other leading universities in competition with middle class and professional children from Tokyo . . . This was the only way these provincial families could have their children compete without handicap in the national educational market.'

A visit to a Japanese classroom holds few surprises. Classes are as overcrowded as those in Britain, and the only notable thing is the discipline of the children which seems to reflect a deep respect for authority. At a later age however, Japanese students often work this off, at least superficially. Their riots are a notable feature of the political scene.

One practical point must be remembered. The Japanese are occupied to a greater extent than most other races by the business of learning their own language and script. As a Japanese journalist said, 'We have to spend a bit more on education than other people because we have three alphabets, whereas most people make do with one.' This makes the virtually 100 per cent literacy figures all the more remarkable.

But it is just about impossible to point to one outstanding reason for Japan's success. If education is to be cited then one must immediately qualify this by saying that it isn't really education itself, but the desire for education as a means to an end. The Japanese as a nation are simply determined to be outstanding in the world and have chosen to achieve this position by economic development. After the Pacific War the military lost face and now the businessman carries the flag.

What about the future? How long will this all last and what happens if the economic miracle stops?

It must be said that, so far, the miracle shows no signs of stopping. The Economic Planning Agency announced in August 1968 that the growth rate in the previous year was 13.3 per cent – real. This exceeded the official target and was the third highest since the war. This was no 'bounce back' after a recession because in 1966 it was also high at 12.3 per cent real. Japanese planners have now had twenty years' experience at keeping it going and are better qualified to do their jobs than anyone else in the world. Nevertheless the planners are merely the jockeys on the horses' backs, and no one can be sure that the animals will not slow up or even take the bit between their teeth and go in the wrong direction.

There are some worrisome features still, in particular Japanese deference to authority. Only a few years ago, the Central Education Council, which advises the Education Minister, presented a report on 'The Image of an Ideal Japanese.' The fact that such a report could be solemnly produced is fairly worrisome but its contents were even worse. It said that loyalty to the State requires that citizens show love for it in the right way. Indifference to the existence of one's own nation, and disregard for its values, amounts to hatred of one's own nation. Other worthy aims for the 'Ideal Japanese' were to regard the family as a focus for leisure and education and to work hard, contribute to social welfare, be creative and adhere to the basic rules. A heartening sign was that the report aroused widespread controversy and was heavily criticised by 'reformist and radical opinion.'

Could the State swing back to authoritarian imperialism and military expansion or will the growth of liberalism and democracy prevent it? This question is difficult to answer but, in brutal geopolitical terms it does not really matter whether the answer is yes or no. The reason is that Japan is more vulnerable to nuclear attack and even to naval blockade than any other country in the world. To provoke one of the big powers from a position outside the hegemony of the United States would be suicide. Japan's centres of population and industry are crowded to a remarkably high density and are even more vulnerable to modern weapons than they were in the Pacific War, and her dependence on overseas raw material supplies is virtually absolute. In foreign policy, she has adopted a so-called 'low posture'. So far the Japanese have had their eyes on only one ball – trade, and it is plain that they don't mind whom they trade with, be it South Africa, Rhodesia, Red China or Cuba.

The Americans want Japan to adopt a more positive foreign policy. In particular they see Japan as a capitalist countervailing force to an increasingly aggressive China. Eventually Japan will be unable to avoid playing a more important role in Far Eastern affairs because she will be so rich. When this time comes it will be interesting to see whether the poor people of Asia regard her as one of their own kind or whether they will see her as Western because of her wealth. Already one can see camera-laden Japanese tourists in Hong Kong or Bombay looking just as rich, uncomprehending and uncomfortable as visiting Westerners. It may well be that money turns out to be thicker than blood.

The Japanese still like to stress their affinity with the Chinese but they are well aware that a third of their trade is with the United States. Increasingly bankers, industrialists, scientists and civil servants talk like Westerners. They may not speak exactly the same language but they know that their problems are likely to be more intelligently discussed in Paris than in Peking.

The alliance with America will probably go on after 1971 when the present treaty expires. The association will probably be loosened but provided such matters as the ownership of Okinawa are amicably settled it seems likely that Japan will go on allowing some American bases on her soil. It would still be unthinkable however for Japan to go as far as providing troops on the anti-communist side in an Asian war.

Although there are powerful forces arguing for greater independence (in spite of the expense) it is difficult to see what else Japan can do but continue some sort of alliance with America. There is one alternative, albeit a perilous one; Japan could make her own nuclear weapons. Happily the very mention of this still causes a shudder strong enough to topple the political career of anyone suspected of thinking about it. Any increase in defence expenditure is more likely to go first to the Imperial Navy, so that at least Japan's trade may be secured without calling out the Americans. Any increase in the size of the conventional army is well down the list. What is the point when China's medium-range nuclear missiles are only 10 minutes' flight time away and Peking is so irrational?

On a more peaceful note Japan may be expected to help more

in what the Foreign Minister delicately calls the North-South problem – the gap between rich and poor. The official line goes as follows (March, 1967, Mr Miki's speech in the Diet): 'In spite of the underdeveloped situation of this country's domestic investment for public works and social development, this country is deeply aware of its moral responsibility, as the only advanced industrial nation in Asia, to address itself seriously to this important North-South question. Particularly in the fields of economic and technical assistance towards countries in Asia, this country wishes to extend as much assistance as possible. For this purpose, the Government is determined to improve, in a positive manner, the domestic system for the promotion of economic co-operation and to strengthen its activities so as to promote positively our economic co-operation with developing countries.'

Already private Japanese industry has spread its net in order to profit by cheaper labour or to ensure long-term supplies of raw materials. Mitsui and Mitsubishi have just set up a forestry development enterprise with Cambodia, and Malaysia, Australia, Fiji, The Philippines and South Korea already contain many Japanese-financed enterprises. The Japanese Government agreed to give Indonesia $80 million worth of economic assistance in 1968. Japanese National Railways pride themselves on training men from developing countries. Japanese know-how in agriculture and fishing is increasingly in demand by such organisations as the FAO. The Japanese tread delicately in all these areas, for memories of the Pacific War persist. But all these developments are welcome in the Pacific, and investments on the Asian mainland will increasingly oblige Japan to take more interest in combating communist influence.

At home, Japan is beginning to attend to the problem of making the islands a better place to live in. The planning is nothing if not bold. First the Economic Planning Agency sets out what the key indicators will be in 1985. The gross national product will be over four times what it was in 1965. Crude steel output will be 180 million annual tons (much larger than that of the US now). The gross capital assets will be eight times the current value and there will be 30 million cars on the road. This latter figure is also eight times the current one and is the most awesome prospect of all.

The Tokyo-Yokohama industrial zone is to be 'scrapped' so far as development is concerned and all new projects will be on the opposite side of Honshu (one assumes the New Tokaido Line extensions will have been installed first). Large areas of the country are designated for stock-raising (to rise threefold compared with 1965) and agriculture. The labour force for this will be half its present size. The plan also envisages recreation belts which are firmly drawn in on the map through some areas which are currently urban. This strip lies along the Pacific Coast from China, east of Tokyo, right round to Southern Kyushu. The fact that planners can adopt such a positive approach to the provision of recreational areas is a heartening sign. Previously it has seemed that, as in Britain, areas of natural beauty were regarded as recreational only until someone wanted to build on them.

The EPA considers that approximately twenty per cent of cumulative gross fixed capital spending in the coming years should be set aside for such large-scale development projects. This will amount to $1.4 trillion – a huge sum of money. The EPA does not mind using the word 'vision' for all this and suggests that an overall agency should be created to supervise these large-scale investments and projects.

Clearly in what the American forecasters call a surprise-free future, and provided the current style of development continues, Japan ought to become the second richest nation in the world. With these riches, she may even become a force for stability, peace and prosperity in her sphere of influence. She will certainly be a beacon of encouragement for the poorer nations of the world. It may be that a close study of her techniques of economic management will reveal something of use to other nations too, some know-how that can be exported even to Western Europe and in particular to the British Isles.

One moral that can be drawn from Japan is after all a simple one, although in practice it may be very difficult to adopt. The moral is this – the Japanese have put economic growth first and foremost on their horizons. Just about everyone in the nation assents to this and works towards this end. Even the Imperial family is aware of it. In a recent 'tanka' competition (poetry rather like the famous haiku, but with thirty-one syllables) held at the Imperial Palace, the Emperor's son, Prince Hitachi, wrote these lines as an expression of what was in his mind.

> *The Shinano flows*
> *Through the mist of rain*
> *And an oil tanker*
> *Is now ready to leave.*

That is modern Japan.

Tables

The following list of tables is in no way comprehensive. It outlines some of the more interesting aspects of the Japanese economy.

TABLE 1

Increasing Rate of Population and the Composition of Age Groups %

Year	Total (1,000 persons)	Increasing Rate for 10 years	Total	Proportion of Age Groups		
				0~14 years old	15~59 years old	60 years old and more
1950	83,200	—	100.0	35.4	56.9	7.7
1960	93,347	12.2	100.0	30.0	61.1	8.9
1970	103,327 (estimated)	10.1	100.0	23.0	66.3	10.7
1980	113,265 (//)	9.6	100.0	22.2	64.8	13.0
1990	118,619 (//)	4.7	100.0	19.2	64.3	16.5

Sources: The Prime Minister's Office and the Institute of Population Problems, Ministry of Health and Welfare.

TABLE 2

Main features of the Income Doubling Plan. (Values at 1958 prices)

	Av. fiscal year 1956–8	Av. fiscal year ests. 1970
Gross National Product (1,000 M. Yen)	9,743	26,000
National Income per head (yen)	87,736	208,600
Industrial production index	100	432
Agric., Forestry & fish produce index	100	144
Exports (US $ million)	2,701	9,320
Imports (US $ million)	3,126	9,891
Energy demands (in coal equivs. '000 tons)	131,815 (1959)	320,760

TABLE 3 SHIPPING

World Tonnage of New Merchant Vessels Launched (in thousands of GT)

	1961	1962	1963	1964	1965
Japan	1,799	2,183	2,367	4,085	5,363
United Kingdom	1,192	1,073	928	1,043	1,073
Sweden	742	841	888	1,021	1,170
West Germany	962	1,010	971	890	1,023
World	7,940	8,375	8,539	10,264	12,216

Note: Figures include vessels of 100 GT or more; Mainland China, East Germany and the USSR are excluded.

Source: Lloyd's Statistics.

TABLE 4 RAILWAYS

Percentage figures showing the distribution of passenger and freight transport between railways and other methods of transport.

% Passenger Transport		% Freight Transport
45.4	Japanese National Railway	30.0
21.3	Private Railways	0.5
1.6	Shipping	43.5
	Planes	—
21.1	Buses	—
—	Trucks	26.0

TABLE 5

Figures showing the steady growth in passengers carried compared to freight carried over the period 1960–65.

	Passengers Carried			*Freight Carried*
	Non-Commuter (millions)	Commuter (millions)	Average per day (thousands)	Tons (millions)
1960	1,784	3,340	14,038	195
1961	1,691	3,593	14,475	206
1962	1,777	3,833	15,368	202
1963	1,878	4,162	16,503	206
1964	1,975	4,434	17,561	207
1965	2,043	4,679	18,415	200

Note: Ten per cent of the route kilometres constitute profitable lines, ninety per cent are unprofitable.
Forty-one per cent of the revenue comes from profitable lines. Fifty-nine per cent comes from lines that make an overall loss.

TABLE 6 CAMERAS

How Japan overhauled West Germany

	JAPAN		WEST GERMANY	
	output	export	output	export
1961	23.5	7.2	25.0	14.0
1962	33.4	10.6	20.5	13.4
1963	43.2	13.0	20.3	13.4
1964	51.6	15.4	22.7	13.4
1965	47.0	20.2	22.8	13.6
1966	43.8	24.1	21.1	12.1

Note: In billions of yen.   **Source:** *Industrial Review of Japan.*

TABLE 7 STEEL

Japan's exports of Iron and Steel

Year	Volume (1,000 tons)	Value ($ million)
1961	2,621	437
1962	4,792	642
1963	5,543	763
1964	7,717	1,081
1965	10,102	1,385
1966	9,666	1,377
1967	10,000	1,417

TABLE 8

Comparison of Steel Exports in 1966 (1,000 tons)

Britain	3,372
West Germany	10,265
France	6,528
Italy	2,078
Belgium, Luxembourg	9,325
Netherlands	2,212
Japan	9,985

TABLE 9

Ratio of LD Converter Steel in percentages

	1965	1966
Japan	55.0	62.6
United States	17.4	25.3
West Germany	19.1	24.5
France	13.1	14.5
Britain	16.5	21.9

TABLE 10 IMPORTS

The Structure of the Import Trade.
(*percentages of total import value*)

	1954	1960	1964	1965
Food, drink and tobacco	**27.2**	**12.2**	**17.5**	**18.0**
Wheat	7.0	3.9	3.3	3.7
Maize	0.6	1.8	2.6	2.8
Sugar	4.5	2.5	3.1	1.9
Raw materials (other than fuel)	**48.0**	**49.2**	**39.0**	**39.4**
Cotton	17.2	9.5	5.5	5.4
Wool	5.5	5.7	4.8	4.3
Ferrous ore and scrap	4.6	9.9	8.3	8.3
Timber	2.0	3.8	5.5	6.0
Non-ferrous ore and concentrates	1.1	3.5	3.0	3.5
Soya beans	2.8	2.4	2.3	2.7
Rubber	1.7	3.2	1.2	1.1
Mineral fuels	**11.1**	**16.5**	**17.7**	**19.9**
Crude oil and products	7.6	12.9	14.5	16.0
Coal	2.6	3.2	2.6	3.3
Manufactured goods	**13.6**	**21.9**	**25.6**	**22.5**
Machine tools	1.0	1.9	1.2	0.8
Office machinery	0.6	1.2	1.7	1.3
Other machinery and vehicles	5.8	5.9	7.5	6.6
Iron and steel	0.4	2.0	2.2	1.7
Non-ferrous metals	1.1	2.3	3.2	3.0
Chemicals	2.7	5.9	5.8	5.0
Others	**0.1**	**0.2**	**0.2**	**0.2**
Value of imports (in million US $)	2399	4491	7938	8167
Quantum (1960=100)	48.6	100.0	175.3	176.6

Sources: Bank of Japan, *Economic State of Japan.*
Ministry of International Trade, *Foreign Trade of Japan.*

G. C. Allen, *Japan as a market and source of supply.*

TABLE 11   IMPORTS

Japan imports most of the raw and processed materials vital to modern industries and part of its food requirements.

Dependence upon Imports by Item[1]   %

Items	1959	1962	1964
Raw cotton (2)	100.0	100.0	100.0
Wool (2)	100.0	100.0	100.0
Dissolved pulp	16.9	29.8	30.3
Iron ore	89.9	95.1	96.4
Bauxite	100.0	100.0	100.0
Copper ore	46.0	84.4	85.4
Raw coal	32.8	50.9	51.4
Crude petroleum	97.9	98.1	98.9
Rice	2.2	1.4	3.4
Wheat	63.0	61.1	74.3

Note: (1) The rate of import is, in principle, calculated on the basis of the imported amount/imported amount +national ouput.

(2) Japan produces a little amount, but its proportion to the imported amount is negligible.

Source: The Ministry of International Trade and Industry.

TABLE 12

Annual rates of growth of Real Gross National Product

	1860–1950	1938–50	1860–1913
United States	3.8	5.7	4.3
Canada	—	5.9	—
United Kingdom	1.8	1.6	2.4
France	1.1	0.2	1.1
Germany	2.4	2.3*	3.0
Netherlands	2.2	1.8	2.3
Switzerland	2.1	2.1	2.6
Sweden	2.0	2.5	2.0
Japan	3.0	−3.0	4.1

Source: Shinohara Miyohei, *Nihonkeizai no Seicho to Junkan*, Tokyo, 1961.

* 1936–52

Bibliography of works consulted

G. C. Allen, *Japan's Economic Expansion*, London (Oxford University Press) 1965

Pat Barr, *The Coming of the Barbarians*, London (Macmillan) 1967

Ralph Hewins, *The Japanese Miracle Men*, London (Secker & Warburg) 1967

S. Okita, *Economic Planning in Japan*, Tokyo (Economic Planning Agency) 1961

David & E. T. Riesman, *Conversations in Japan*, London (Allen Lane, The Penguin Press) 1967

Richard Storry, *A History of Modern Japan*, Harmondsworth (Penguin) 1968

'Economist', *Consider Japan*, London (Duckworth) 1963

Space in Japan, Tokyo (Science and Technology Agency) 1967

The Iron and Steel Industry of Japan, London (The Iron and Steel Institute) 1963

The Japan of Today, Tokyo (Ministry of Foreign Affairs) 1965

Japanese Industry, Tokyo (Foreign Capital Research Society, Bank of Japan) 1966

Japanese National Railways: A general description, Tokyo (Japanese National Railways) 1966

Technical Aspects of the New Tokaido Line, Tokyo (Japanese National Railways) 1966

Education in Japan, Tokyo (Ministry of Education) 1967

Japan Trade Guide, Tokyo (Jiji Press) 1963/4

Industrial Review of Japan, Tokyo (Nihon Keizai Shimbun) 1968

The Motor Ship, Supplement to 'Japanese Shipbuilding', London (IPC) 1967

Tokyo Newsletters, London (Department of Education and Science – reports from the British Government's Science Attaché in Tokyo)

Statistical Handbooks of Japan, Tokyo (Bureau of Statistics, Office of the Prime Minister)

Review of National Science Policy – Japan, Paris (OECD) 1967

Periodicals

Science and Technology in Japan (quarterly), Tokyo (Asahi Evening News)

Wing International (monthly), Tokyo (Koku Shimbun-Sha)

Information Bulletin (annual), Tokyo (Ministry of Foreign Affairs)

Japan Society of London Bulletin (three times a year)

Economic Statistics (monthly), Tokyo (Bank of Japan)

Economic Statistics (annual), Tokyo (Bank of Japan)

Economic Survey of Japan (annual), Tokyo (Economic Planning Agency)

Foreign Trade of Japan (annual), Tokyo (Japan External Trade Organization)

Japan Statistical Yearbook (annual), Tokyo (Prime Minister's Office)

Fuji Bank Bulletin (quarterly), Tokyo

Quarterly Revisions, London (Anglo-Japanese Economic Institute)

OECD Observer (monthly), Paris (OECD)

Index